WOMEN ARE LIKE EARTH

To Mitzi with love!
Goddess in me sees Goddess in you!
Anna Markolina
2022

Creative Journey Publishing, Sammamish, 2022

Creative Journey Publishing, Sammamish, WA, 2022

The book contains concepts and practices of the Universal Healing Tao created and developed by Mantak Chia. References to Mantak Chia's works can be found in the bibliography section.

Cover art: "Divine Feminine" by Dr. Alisha C. Halverson
Edited by Beáta Jachulski Baker.
Illustrations by Carol Francis.
Jacket design by JD&J Design LLC
Formatting by Polgarus Studio

ISBN: 978-0-578-99793-3

Library of Congress Control Number: 2022900074

Creative Journey Publishing, Sammamish, 2022

WOMEN ARE LIKE EARTH

Becoming Vital Through Feminine Energy Cultivation

Anna Margolina, PhD

Creative Journey Publishing, Sammamish, WA, 2022

Contents

Dr. Anna Margolina, PhD. Portrait by Carol Francis, 2021.

A Letter from Dr. Anna:

Dear YOU:

I am thrilled to bring you proven and practical ways to love your body, and embrace your ageless beauty and sacred sexuality. You — and those around you — will delight in your radiance.

Those who attend my classes and workshops notice increased vibrancy and playfulness, and a deeper connection to their flowing creativity. You will too. So enjoy each exciting exercise as you expand your natural curiosity and awareness in every way.

Let the journey to Becoming Vital Through Feminine Energy Cultivation begin NOW!

Anna Margolina, PhD

Disclaimer!

Attention! The practices presented in this book are not a substitute for medical treatment, nor should they be used to treat or diagnose any medical condition. You are advised to seek personal instructions with a certified instructor of the Universal Healing Tao. Refer to https://www.universaltaoinstructors.com/ to find an instructor in your area. The author, Anna Margolina and Creative Journey Publishing, LLC are not responsible for any consequences stemming from doing the practices on your own or not following instructions correctly. You are responsible for your own choices. If you have any physical or mental conditions which require medical care, please seek qualified medical advice.

Preface

Why Crawl When You Can Fly?

"I can't explain myself, I'm afraid," said Alice, "because I'm not myself, you see."
"I don't see," said the Caterpillar.

Have you tried to explain yourself?

For many, turning 50 years old opens a strange life chapter. Your body undergoes major restructuring. As one woman said, "It's like watching pieces of you fall away." Coming of age might be the most important journey of your life.

I was 45 when I first decided to investigate which changes in my body are inevitable and natural: and which I can postpone, avoid, or reverse. In other words: How do I slow down biological aging and create a fulfilling, meaningful, and youthful way of being after the age of 50? This exploration led me to birth my self-care business, "Ageless with Anna." I realized that I do not have to accept other people's ideas of how I should be as I mature. Instead, I decided to learn how to fly. Perhaps you would like to learn too?

Begin by asking yourself:

How do I want to show up in my life?

How do I want to grow?

How can I best flow with change or challenge?

How do I want to walk the road called my life?

How can I best harness the energy of my mind to remain vibrant?

The energy of the mind is real. It's the essence of life that shines out of your eyes and illuminates your face. Unlike your physical body, your energy is timeless, and uplifts your spirit. Your mind is your personal Wonderland. When you know who you are in your Wonderland, you no longer feel any need to explain yourself to caterpillars. Then you can use your energy to rebirth yourself, let go of limitations, and fly!

Emerging from the cocoon.

Introduction

The Wake-Up Call:
Burnout Blessings and Rebirth

I grew up in Russia in a family of scientists. They were my mom and dad; I was not a science experiment. My mom was a PhD in Chemistry and my dad was a PhD in Physics. As you can see, I was destined to become a scientist and follow in their footsteps.

I grew up in a house filled with books. There were books in every room, and my favorite room was one with sturdy wooden bookshelves from the floor all the way to the ceiling. As a child I used to climb these bookshelves like a tiny Spider-Man, looking for a book I hadn't read yet. Nobody cared which books I read, so I consumed a curious mix of romance, popular science, academic science, mystery, sci-fi, poetry, decadent novels, philosophy, and mysticism. I always loved animals and read a lot of books about them. Among my treasured possessions was a big book bound in a thick red cover titled Red Book (also known as Red Data Book of Russian Federation.). On page after page there were pictures of various animals – mammals, birds, reptiles, amphibians, and insects – which were disappearing from the face of the earth due to industrial farming, road construction, urban sprawl, hunting, and fishing. I felt sad and hopeless. Even as a child I understood there was very little to be done to stop this new wave of extinction unless we, as a human race, learned to cherish, love, and replenish our Earth. I couldn't help but wonder how adults (who were supposedly more knowledgeable and intelligent than children) couldn't see that as an animal species, we humans depended on clean water, breathable air, and the availability of spacious green landscapes populated by various life forms.

My own book of life had a plot twist from the very beginning. Very soon after I was born my parents divorced, and my mom became a single mother in the big city of Moscow where she had no relatives. Being an ambitious young scientist, she eventually made the tough decision to place me in a boarding school.

In Soviet Russia a boarding school was not a prestigious institution for rich kids. It was a place for kids who came from broken homes with parents who were abusive, financially broke, or alcoholics. So at the tender age of 7, an intelligent, gentle, and naïve Anna found herself in a jungle. I was a shy, awkward, and nearsighted girl with a stutter, so very soon I found myself a target for bullies. Fortunately I learned to sneak outside of the school's grounds and find solace and friendship in the company of stray dogs. I also met a girl named Olga, one year older than I was, who became my best friend and loyal protector. Books, dogs, and Olga saved my childhood.

In the 5th grade I returned to a regular school and started coming home every afternoon just like everybody else. But I didn't feel like everybody else. I felt like an alien who suddenly landed among earthlings, and now had to figure out how to be a human. I stuttered severely and felt extremely awkward in the company of other kids. But I had a few good friends, I had plenty of books, and I also had my own dog: a gorgeous German Shepherd who accompanied me on long walks in the forest. I never stuttered when I talked to my dog. I still think dogs are the best listeners. They do not judge. (Cats are a very different story.)

My mother did her best to solve my stuttering problem. Over the years I was seen by many specialists, including one psychiatrist. I loved talking to him. He was a soft-spoken, intelligent, and highly educated man. We discussed my dreams, my relationships, and my emotional issues. And every week he adjusted my medications. You know how some people start taking drugs when they go to college. I stopped taking drugs when I went to college. My reason was that I was accepted to the Russian Medical University where I began to study pharmacology and physiology. Apparently some of the medications so generously prescribed by my psychiatrist to calm my nerves had very serious side effects. So down the drain they went. That resulted in the return of all my emotional problems and my stuttering. But I still thought that was better than taking those pills.

I graduated from the Russian Medical University with a degree in Medical Biophysics, and even went on to get a PhD in Biology. Upon graduating I was fortunate to secure a dream job. I became a writer, scientific editor, and researcher with the Russian Cosmetics and Medicine Journal. It was during my years working for the Cosmetics and Medicine Journal that I acquired a deep knowledge and respect for our skin. Until then, I believed aging was something unpleasant but inevitable. But the more I researched skin science, the more I realized that as human beings we have a lot of options in choosing how we want to age. I learned to take better care of my skin, and protect it from influences which might accelerate aging. I learned that wanting to have youthful, radiant, and glowing skin is not vanity; it is a sane desire to live in a healthy and vibrant body.

Then, at the peak of my career, I walked away from all of it. I got married and moved to the United States of America. At 33, I was young and naïve, and I didn't realize I had just uprooted my entire life and would have to transplant it into new ground.

Have you ever gone through the experience of starting a new chapter? In America, I not only had to learn how to speak and write in English, become familiar with a new culture and customs, and drive a car (which I didn't in Russia); I also had to figure out what to do with my life — and with my brain. While in search of new directions and personal healing — and still struggling with stuttering — I discovered the magic of hypnotherapy. I was mesmerized. I had always considered my stuttering and emotional problems as something permanent, like the color of my eyes or the shape of my nose. But here was a modality which magically changed how I felt and responded, and which accomplished it in a very short time — without medications or side effects. In 2012, at the age of 45, my stuttering was finally reduced to a negligible level. I gained so much speaking confidence I won a humorous speech contest in my Toastmasters District!

I felt uplifted and elated. I felt I had discovered something magical (yet real and practical) which could help me solve my emotional issues and heal my mind and my heart. I wanted to share this magic with others. So I decided to become a hypnotherapist. I took all the necessary certification classes; probably more than I needed, but I love to learn. I got my hypnotherapist's license, and I opened my own business.

There was only one problem with this plan: I had zero business experience. I had no idea what it took to run a successful business with real clients; I was terrible at time management and sales; and I believed all I needed to do was work hard, dream big, lean in, and never give up. It was not enough to succeed. Within the first two years of being in business I was overweight, overworked, overwhelmed, and burned out emotionally and physically.

Have you ever found yourself working way too hard and neglecting your own needs? Sacrificing your sleep, pleasure, and fun? Pressing forward like a stubborn soldier who does not believe in giving up? This is where I was. During those two years I even had to undergo three surgeries. I knew I had to stop and rethink what I was doing. Sometimes the Universe gives you a wakeup call. It is not always a gentle nudge. With a blend of regret and relief I closed my first hypnotherapy business, and set out on a path to recovery and revision. In hindsight I know my burnout was a blessing. If not for the sense of being broken and sick, sluggish and slow, depressed and disinterested, heavy and — well, old — I would not have the determination and desperation to invest into studying and practicing methods of restoring and amplifying my vitality and vibrancy.

We Are Nature

Paradoxically, it was not before I nearly destroyed my own spirit and body in the pursuit of material goods that I realized what the depletion of the Earth (which had so upset me as a child) and the depletion of my body (which I experienced as an adult) both had in common. It was treating the nature outside of our bodies and the nature *of* our own body as a disposable resource. In order to change this we have to stop thinking about nature as a resource and start thinking about ourselves as nature.

I was able to change my own story and switch from depletion and destruction to replenishment and nourishment, because I learned there was another way. On my search for healing, I came across the teachings of ancient Taoist Masters who, over 5,000 years ago, came to a curious realization that we are not separate from our planet and the Universe. They developed powerful practices for the mind, body, and spirit, which allow a dedicated student to restore and replenish their own vitality, cultivate personal powers; and start living in harmony with their own self, other people, and the environment. It was a completely new way of thinking about my body, my mind, and the planet Earth.

The Two Frogs Story

Once upon a time, there were two frogs. They were hopping happily through a sunny garden until both of them fell into a bucket full of cream.

"Oh no, we're doomed! Now we're going to die!" said the first frog, Negative Nelly.

"Oh, please don't say that! Let's paddle and kick and see if we can escape!" said the second frog, Positive Pammy.

9

"Pammy! Are you crazy? Paddle and kick? What good will it do? We will just exhaust ourselves and then die anyway. We might as well give up now!"

And with those words Negative Nelly stopped struggling and drowned.

But Positive Pammy kept paddling and kicking while giving herself little motivational talks.

"Come on, Pammy! You can do it!"

And something strange happened. The cream started getting thicker. And then it was solid. The frog churned all the cream into butter. She was able to make a big leap and escape.

Are you with Negative Nelly, and believe after a certain age there's no use in putting any effort into feeling sexy, beautiful, and vibrant? Do you believe that trauma and past experiences define you? Or are you with Positive Pammy, and want to keep paddling and kicking? Whatever your answer, give yourself an A+ and keep reading on.

Chapter 1

The Dark Enlightenment:
Discovering Taoist Ageless Practices

Do you agree that we have a curious attitude toward our own body? Intellectually we know that it is made of flesh and blood, and therefore can be injured, damaged, and wounded. Yet we act as if admitting our own humanity is a weakness and something to be ashamed of while, conversely, acting as if treating our own bodies as disposable is some sort of virtue.

In January 2015, I was on a plane flying to Thailand.

What do people typically do in Thailand? They bask in the sun, savor delicious food, and see the elephants. My plan was to sit in the dark for a week. I was going to attend a Taoist Dark Room Retreat with a world-famous instructor, Master Mantak Chia.

It all began when I read a book written by Master Chia in which he talked about emotions as energy. In this book he suggested that some emotions nourish and rejuvenate our bodies, while other emotions are like bitter medicine: you take them when you need them, but too much can be poisonous. This was a message that could have been written just for me. I was listening.

And now I was on a plane flying halfway around the world to go sit in a dark room.

(When I told a friend about this she said, "Anna, why didn't you tell me this is your fancy? I have a really dark basement. You can sit there for free!")

Imagine a red brick building surrounded by lush greenery. Picture all the windows blocked by thick black panels; not even a speck of light can penetrate. Imagine walking through a long corridor lined with layers of heavy, velvety black curtains. Imagine spending a week in pitch-black darkness, without your phone, books, or TV. No conversation. This was my week. Days and nights blended together and rolled by as I listened and followed Master Chia's teachings. I remember lying in the dark, feeling so deeply relaxed I felt I was floating. Nothing to see. Nothing to which to respond. No urgent tasks to complete. I remember waking up and not knowing if I was awake or still dreaming. I remember combing my hair and then laughing. Who was going to see me? I still took showers and brushed my teeth, but dressing up and styling my hair received minimal effort.

One day it was time to go outside. I was told to go out at night and take my sunglasses. Sunglasses at night? OK!

I moved through the layers of heavy black curtains. Suddenly a bright light hit my eyes. I put on my sunglasses. And I stepped out into moonlight. The full moon was shining in the midnight sky. Every leaf and every blade of grass was illuminated by this silvery light. I filled my lungs with deliciously fresh air. Frogs were singing their love songs in the distance. I felt vibrantly alive. I was at home in my body, supported by vibrant energy. All my senses were wide open, soaking in every bit of every divine moment.

When the morning came and my eyes adjusted to the sunlight, I was still walking around like a tourist marveling at every little wonder of life. I sat at a breakfast table. In the Dark Room meals had been simple and minimal. Here in the daylight, I put the first morsel of food in my mouth. A Universe of taste exploded on my palate. I remembered how throughout most of my life I was gobbling food without chewing, trying to save every moment for work. Now, I was savoring my meal mindfully. It was delightful.

This was the first time I realized I have a body, and that my body can be a source of delicious sensations I never realized were available to me.

Taoist Ageless Technology

More than 5,000 years ago in China there were wise sages who wanted to understand nature and the Universe. We now call them the Taoist Masters. You can call them the first scientists. Unlike scientists of the West who believed they had to take things apart in order to study them, Taoist sages studied things as they were: in life and motion. They believed in the power of observation and meditation. They eventually were able to discover the hidden laws which govern the Universe. Today, modern science has come surprisingly close to the ideas and concepts developed by Taoist sages who did not have any technology. They only had their own bodies, senses, and minds.

The ancient Tao Masters looked at a flowing river and then at a stagnant pond, "Oh, look — when the flow is abundant and strong, the water tastes fresh and sweet... Hmm, the stagnant water tastes foul and unpleasant. It breeds illnesses. It lacks freshness and vibrancy." They would notice the wind blowing through the trees and think, "We cannot see the wind, but we can feel it on our skin. We can see the trees and the grasses move when the wind blows through them." And they compared it to an invisible force flowing through the human body, giving it vitality and life. They eventually made a connection between the flowing river and the playful, and sparkling energy of a young person, and the stagnant pond and the sluggish and lifeless energy of an old or sick person.

They would observe how a very **material** pile of wood could be transformed by fire into **immaterial** light and heat. And they speculated that within living tissues there must be a process of converting the materials of the body into the fire of life. In young people this fire burns lively, bright, and strong. It shines through their eyes, illuminates their skin, and gives power and passion to their thoughts and emotions. In older people this fire starts to die out, until all the burning coals are covered with ashes. They concluded that all life on Earth, including humans, has something which animates the physical body and makes it alive. They called this force Chi (Qi) or "life force."

Many wellness and spirituality practices make the mistake of either focusing solely on the physical body, or disregarding the body entirely and only dealing with spiritual essences. Some spiritual practices go as far as to advocate "mortifying" the flesh and beating the physical body into submission through pain, starvation, and hard work. Many religions condemn and forbid expressions of sexuality — especially feminine sexuality — considering it "dirty," "shameful," and "sinful." Taoists discovered our body is not just a physical structure entrapping our spiritual essence. It is a container for our energy, and it is the medium through which our energy flows. It is also a receiver and generator for energy which animates it. Life continues as long as the body can sustain the flow of Chi.

Through embracing the wonders of the physical body with its blood, sweat, pains, imperfections, emotions, cravings, and desires, Taoists discovered a new way of living and being in their bodies which still fascinates scientists and medical doctors. Through experimentation and observation (and centuries before modern scientific discoveries) they developed surprisingly effective practices for maintaining vitality and enhancing the health and resilience of the body, while developing and expanding mastery of the mind. Their teachings became the foundation for modern Chinese medicine and martial arts. This is not surprising, since both doctors and fighters needed practical knowledge and powerful results more than beautiful theories and convincing ideas. In ancient China, a physician who could not cure himself would lose all his patients — and often, his life. A martial arts practitioner who wanted to live beyond their prime fighting years had to know how to supplement ordinary muscle power with unordinary mental, emotional, and spiritual strength.

I have been deeply interested in Chinese medicine and martial arts ever since I watched my first Kung Fu movie, but didn't know how to take practical steps in acquiring this knowledge. It seemed too difficult to attain. I first enrolled in a Tai Chi class when I moved to the United States of America. And I found I was right: It was not easy to master Tai Chi. So when my son was born, I stopped attending classes and soon returned to enjoying graceful and powerful movements of Tai Chi masters from a couch, watching TV.

It was not until 2015, when I decided to travel to Thailand and study Qigong from a modern Taoist Master, Mantak Chia, that I realized I had finally found a practice to which I could commit. Master Mantak Chia began studying with his own Taoist Master when was very young. He went on to learn Western medicine and science while continuing his study and practice of Taoist Qigong. He eventually developed the Universal Healing Tao system, which is rooted in ancient Taoist teachings. But it also has a sound scientific foundation, and is straightforward enough to grasp —even by a busy modern Western student who doesn't have the luxury of spending a lifetime in a remote mountain sanctuary being guided by a wise guru.

At first the Tao system seemed to be just an interesting idea, a belief, a theory, and a bit of a fairy tale — which I wasn't sure I truly believed in. But the more I practiced it, the more I was impressed by the results. I loved it so much it became my daily spiritual practice. Today these practices are an integral part of my path to becoming more authentic, alive, and vital. I am a hypnotherapist, so I started adding Taoist meditative practices to my hypnotherapy sessions. My clients loved how it helped them to recover their lost spark and a feeling of vitality and vibrancy.

This book contains Taoist ageless practices of the Universal Healing Tao system. They are based on the original teachings of the ancient Tao Masters in China, further developed by my teacher, Master Chia, and tried and tested by me. I am reviewing just the basic Taoist practices, which are easy to learn and are generally safe to practice on your own. (This means you are not going to go beyond the range of activities you are comfortable doing.) As a scientist,

I made sure that every practice I present in this book makes sense from a scientific perspective. However, since we all are different and have different bodies and physical abilities, please make sure you listen to your body and seek qualified medical advice if you have any underlying health conditions.

I encourage you to approach this book with curiosity, an open mind, and the willingness to learn. Experiment with the practices I present. Notice what works, and let go of what you do not enjoy. You are also encouraged to continue and deepen your practice with a certified instructor of the Universal Healing Tao. And if you are curious about using hypnosis to accelerate your journey to vitality through Taoist practices presented in this book, please, feel free to contact me at anna@agelesswithanna.com.

This book is for you if you have a desire to become vital and vibrant, and are looking for simple and effective practices you can easily incorporate into your life. This book is also for you if you wish to discover the secrets of ageless beauty beyond cosmetic products and procedures. Finally, this book is for every woman who wants to heal physically, emotionally, and spiritually, and wants to learn how to harness her life force and direct it to healing and restoration.

Taoist philosophy and practices transformed my life, my mind, and my body. The idea of Chi, or life force, which feeds every cell in my body including my brain cells, was something I had never considered before. I suddenly could see how ridiculous my behavior was. I needed my body for everything I aspired to accomplish – including a thriving business. And I was on a course of ruining my body for the sake of succeeding in business. I discovered I was not alone in my folly. Many people, especially women, balk at the idea that taking care of their physical body is just as important (in fact, more important) than taking care of their houses, families, professional projects, and gardens. Many clients who have come to me to learn the Taoist secrets of feminine vitality and sexuality have reached a point where they've pushed themselves way too far. They could no longer enjoy or digest their food; they could no longer feel desire or sexual pleasure; and they felt their mental and physical faculties were in shambles. This is a sad but inevitable consequence of placing too much importance on material goods while neglecting spiritual gifts, emotional connections, and physical vitality.

A woman's body is like earth. It is replenished with positive nurturing energy. A woman's body needs love, sexual desire, laughter, and joy the same way garden soil needs water and sunshine. However, we cannot become more positive by trying to be more positive. The secret to more vibrancy is in understanding how our body generates, moves and transforms matter and energy.

Let's Do This!

Answer the following questions:

1. What makes you feel alive?
2. What do you do for fun? What do you like about it?
3. Think of the three most delightful memories in your life, and let yourself mentally step into each of them. What do you see, feel, hear, smell, and taste in these memories? How does your body respond to reliving these memories?
4. Have you ever been in love? How does love feel within your body?
5. When do you feel you're expressing yourself most authentically?

What did you notice when you went through these questions? How did answering these questions affect your body?

Whether you have an abundance of vibrant, fun, and loving memories or struggled with each question, celebrate yourself and give yourself an A+.

You are going to learn how to create vibrant, flowing, and rejuvenating energy in your body — and it will be easier than you ever imagined. Being vibrant and vital is your birthright. Your body knows how to feel and dwell in delight. You are learning how to claim what is rightfully yours.

Chapter 2

Inner Alchemy of Youth and Beauty

I stood in front of a mirror and scrutinized my face for signs of wrinkles. I was 14. When I told my mother I was afraid to age, she told me a story. A famous 17th century French courtesan, Ninon de L'Enclos, was dancing with King Louis XIV, who was known for his gallantry and romantic adventures.

"You are a goddess. I am losing my mind," whispered the King right into her delicate ear.

"Oh, your Majesty!" smiled the divine Ninon. "You flatter me, but...listen, I wouldn't tell this to any other man...but I am nearing 60."

Now as I myself near the age of 60, this story is not as fascinating as it was when I was 14. Many modern women in America are youthful, vibrant, and sexy at that age. However, back in the Soviet Union where women tended to lose their beauty and vitality by the age of 40, the story of a French courtesan impressed me beyond words. I was intrigued and inspired. All of a sudden my fear of aging was replaced by the determination to crack the code of ageless beauty.

Many years later, I found a paperback book titled *Life, Letters, and Epicurean Philosophy of Ninon de L'Enclos, the Celebrated Beauty of the Seventeenth Century*. Ninon de L'Enclos was a real person, not an invention. She shared the stage of history with the illustrious King Louis XIV, and was a close friend of his second wife, Madame de Maintenon. Ninon continued to inspire passion in others until a very advanced age. Among her passionate admirers was Abbe de Gedoine, a 25-year-old attractive gallant who spent months trying to win Ninon's heart. Finally she agreed to see him in her boudoir.

"Oh, Ninon!" exclaimed the young man. "Why did you torture me for so long? Why only today have you allowed me to come to see you?"

"Well," replied the divine Ninon, leisurely lounging on a sofa in her most seductive gown. "I must admit, it came from vanity. I always fancied to have a lover at my fourscore, and just yesterday I turned 80 years old."

One poet said of Ninon: "The god of love was hiding in the wrinkles on her forehead." Another who knew Ninon described her very special beauty this way:

"She had every address of coquetry, with all the spirit of gallantry; her whole air was capable of inspiring the warmest sentiments…and she herself seemed to breathe the same passion with which she inspired her admirers."

Ninon De L'Enclos. Parts of an etching by **Antoine-Jean-Baptiste Coupé** (1784 -ca. 1852) (Image is in public domain)

Could that ever be you? Might be your approach to love and relationships would be different, and might be not everybody is dreaming about having a passionate lover at the age of 80. But I am speaking about confidence, vitality, and ageless beauty. Do you see yourself possessing these qualities at the age of 80 and beyond?

One of my clients said, "At the rate I am burning myself out, I might not live to 80."

Hopefully, this is not your story.

The Difference Between Boys and Girls

When I was little and inquisitive, I asked my mother:

"Mom, what is the difference between a boy and a girl?"

"Well, Anna, a boy is bigger and stronger."

"But mom, what if we are talking about a very big and strong girl and a very small and weak boy?"

"Anna, boys like to climb trees and play with toy guns and cars."

"But mom, what about girls who like to climb trees and play with toy guns and cars?"

Finally, my mother had enough.

"Anna, stop pestering me. When a boy grows up, he will grow a beard and a girl will not."

I wish my mother had talked to me about the birds and the bees. But I don't blame her. Sex is a touchy topic.

When I grew up and became a student of female sexuality and spirituality, I finally learned the difference between a boy and a girl.

Most boys learn to be proud of their penises.

Most girls learn to be ashamed of their vaginas.

I wish I had learned how to feel proud of having a female body.

I wish I had learned my sexual organs are vital and important organs, and they deserve respect, love, and care.

I wish my doctor had told me the aging of my body is not a medical issue, and that I can delay and even reverse many unpleasant symptoms of menopause.

I wish I had known I could exercise my sexual organs in a way that does not have to feel "dirty" (or even include sex). I wish I had known I don't have to wait for a perfect lover to confirm I'm worthy of worshipping and saturating my body with divine pleasure.

I wish I had known it's not sinful or dirty to touch my body and learn how to ignite its synapses for pleasure. I also wish I had known I could exercise my pelvic floor the same way I exercise any other muscles, and choose whether to make it sexually pleasurable or just enjoyable and fun.

Today, I teach women the secrets of sexual vitality because I believe sexual energy is like the water which nourishes our beauty garden. When you start tapping into this rich source, your radiance and vibrancy come to life.

There is No Sex in The Soviet Union

When Mikhail Gorbachev (the last president of the Soviet Union) started Perestroika and Glasnost, lifted the Iron Curtain, and ended the Cold War between America and Russia, the whole country watched the first-ever teleconference between America and Russia. Wow, finally! Real American people were talking to real Russian people!

It was translated live and uncensored, which explains why the following question was allowed rather than being permanently erased from this event: "Could you tell us about sex and sexual education in the Soviet Union?"

There was an awkward silence on the Russian end. Then one female voice said with absolute conviction, "There is no sex in the Soviet Union. There never was, and never will be."

As someone living in the Soviet Union I can tell you: There was sex. But we didn't talk about it.

If you had the same question about sexual education in the Soviet Union, here is how it was handled in my school.

One day we girls were giggly and excited, because our art teacher told all the boys to go play outside while we were gathered up into the classroom. She shut the doors, and said she wanted to have a "girl chat" with us. First, she told us how important it was to keep our female organs warm. "If you get an inflammation and your fascia fuses together, you might have a harder time conceiving a baby." She probably was instructed to give us more sexual health tips, but she just couldn't stay with the topic and soon we started gossiping about men.

"Girls, you need to know when men reach the age of 40, they start falling in love with women half their age."

She shook her head and added with a soft, rich chuckle, "Oh, my. One day he is a respectable and loyal husband, and then suddenly he goes crazy and wants to leave his wife. Oh, girls! They just cannot resist the feeling of sexiness and arousal. It's like a drug for them."

I took notice. Ever since that day, I made sure I wore warm pants to keep my female parts cozy and healthy, and I vowed to stay young and sexy.

I wish I realized much earlier the sacredness of my sexual organs. Not because they can help me keep my man attracted to me, but just because they are **my** organs in **my** body creating **my** magic. I wish had learned how to replenish and rejuvenate my feminine energy, my mind, and my spirit.

What messages did you receive about your body as a child? Did you learn to cherish and celebrate your femininity, or did you learn to be ashamed of your "private parts?" What messages did you receive about relationships? Did you learn to respect each other's boundaries and sovereignty, or did you learn to manipulate and coerce? Did you learn trust or fear? Did you learn to be open about your feelings, or did you learn to suppress and disown them?

The stories which were woven into the fabric of your neurology as a child determine your actions, reactions, and choices as an adult. The good news is: If you are not happy with what you learned, you can unlearn it and learn something new.

Women Are Like Earth

Remember all the stupid things you did when you were younger? Thank your body for this. And think how wonderful it is your body — the same body you had when you were young — is still here serving you.

Aging is something we accept as inevitable. But a lot of what we call aging is not aging. A lot of what we call aging is our mental state manifesting itself in our body; presenting itself through our skin, facial expressions, movements, posture, and the overall vibe we convey.

If you are a successful, ambitious woman who works in a highly stressful, demanding, unforgiving, and often toxic corporate environment, you might have to push through exhaustion and pain on a daily basis. You might have to drive yourself to the edge trying to perform on the level required to keep your job. You might have children, aging parents, relatives, and charity work which also require your energy. If you continue ignoring your energy, you might come to a point where you have no energy left to feel sexy and vibrant. Your emotions might go haywire. You might struggle to keep your negative emotions under control. You also might notice you no longer vibrate at a sensual touch, and it's getting really difficult to have phenomenal orgasms. When a woman with a body in the energy poorhouse keeps spending like an energy billionaire, she risks exhausting her energy fortune and going deeper into energy debt.

Unfortunately, most women who push through to exhaustion fail to notice they are no longer energy billionaires. So they keep unconsciously adjusting their lives, not noticing how joy, passion, freedom of moving their body, laughter, adventure, and (yes) sexual desire diminish and eventually die out. If they notice they no longer get excited about things which used to excite them, they think, "Of course — it's old age. It happens to everyone. It's just the way things are."

I learned that a woman's body is like earth. It can continue growing beautiful flowers on one condition: It has to be replenished and taken care of. When you apply the philosophy of aggressive industrial farming to your body (taking on more and more, using stimulants and poisons to get even more out of an already exhausted body) you will end with a depleted, dry, and devastated body. The waters of sexual pleasure will stop flowing. The flowers of life and love will no longer bloom.

There is a simple truth: If you are breathing and moving, you have enough energy to turn your life around. You just need to learn how to stop depleting your life force, and how to start replenishing and regenerating your vitality. The choice is yours. You can be sad, grumpy, dull, frail, dependent, and unattractive. Or you can be fun, vibrant, sexy, enthusiastic, and alluring. You get to decide whether you want to decline and deteriorate; or remain active, vibrant, and beautiful while you grow in wisdom, compassion, and love.

Let's Do This!

1. Rub your hands together.

2. Hold them close to each other, palms facing. Relax and cup your palms as if holding an invisible ball.

3. Start slowly moving your hands apart, and moving them close together. Imagine the invisible ball getting bigger and smaller.

4. Did you notice how your hands started feeling resistance when you moved them closer? As you continue doing this exercise, the feeling will become stronger. You will feel there is something there. The more you focus on imagining a ball of energy between your hands, the more you will feel it. Now slowly without touching your skin move your palms over your face as if washing it with invisible water. What did you notice?

Recognizing others and yourself as another beautiful creative expression, like a rose, might inspire quite amazing interactions of respect.

Carol Francis

Chapter 3

Your Energy Matters: The Yin and Yang of Sacred Feminine Vitality

In one of the classic Taoist stories a student asks the Tao master, "Master, how I can keep my energy strong even at a very old age?" The Master brings him to the Yellow River and says, "You see this water? When you figure out how to make it flow uphill, you will get it."

The student thinks, "Huh? Uphill? How is that possible? Everyone knows rivers flow downhill." Then the student remembers his home village, and the waterwheel people used to bring the water uphill.

~A story told by Master Mantak Chia

Modern science has discovered we have our own "Yellow River" inside your body — a river of liquid gold. It is our energy; our bioelectricity. This river is what moves, animates, and illuminates our body. It is the fabric from which our mind, soul, and spirit are made. It is our life force, flowing through every cell and fiber of our body. It is a flickering flame inside every cell keeping us alive.

As the ancient Taoist Masters discovered, the same river of electricity flows through all living things. It animates a blade of grass, a tree, a small furry creature, a frog, a bird, and a human being equally. This river flows through your body, making it vibrant and alive. It's the same river and it follows the same rules. This river creates the passion you breathe, and the fire that keeps you vibrant and inspired. When we are young and healthy we have the luxury of energy wealth. Some amount of neglect and depletion can be easily tolerated. When we get older, the body needs to pay its energy bills. The repair cost skyrockets. A 4-year-old bounces off the walls, opens every drawer, and generally delights in their own body and movements. With age the body gets colder, slower, and weaker, and generally becomes a source of various pains and aches. A 70-year-old might prefer to sit or lie down rather than explore a new environment. The ancient Tao Masters wanted to continue their studies until a very old age, so they started developing practices and ways of thinking which could keep their river of life — Chi — flowing abundantly rather than becoming stagnant, depleted, and polluted.

What if you discovered a way to direct the flow of your life force/Chi to nourish and uplift your entire body?

Chi and How to Get More of It

Taoists distinguished three main types of Chi. The first is Cosmic Chi, or the source Chi, which animates and sets in motion everything in this world. This is the primordial creative force which is present in all material and immaterial objects and living organisms. Next is Universal Chi, which is the energy generated by the planets and stars. Finally there is Earth Chi, which is flowing through everything on our planet, including our bodies. Everything which is moving and alive has Chi. The difference between Chi and the electromagnetic energy which illuminates our houses or powers up our cell phones is that the bio-electromagnetic energy is produced by living cells. Think of your body as a lantern shining its light. Every lantern needs a source of energy. Your body is no different. When your energy starts running out, your light goes out.

Just like a puppet moved by the hand of a puppeteer, your body moves when it is animated by the bioelectricity running through every cell, nerve, and tissue. Your mind is a puppeteer directing and controlling this bioelectricity. Yet the mind itself is made of a special form of electromagnetic energy, which is called conscious electromagnetic energy.

Taoists believed we have three bodies: the physical body, the energy body, and the information body.

Let's explore these three bodies.

Look around for five things you can see. **Look at them.** Then find five things you can **touch. Touch them.** Close your eyes and **listen** to the sounds around you. Can you identify five sounds? Are there any **smells**? What **tastes** do you have in your mouth right now? You just experienced signals from your **physical body** through your eyes, skin, ears, nose, and tongue.

Take a deep breath. Feel the air moving through your nostrils and traveling into your lungs. Put your hand on your heart and feel your heartbeat. Your body constantly talks to you. You might not always notice the hair on your head or the clothes against your skin, but your body provides you with a world of sensations.

Now notice your **energy.** Realize you have an intuitive ability to feel energy. Are you energetic and alive, or exhausted and depleted? Stand up and vigorously shake your arms and your body. Stand still and feel into your body. Do you notice anything moving? Your energy body is speaking to you.

Next, look around the room and **mentally label** things you see. Notice the table, the lamp, the ceiling, etc. These names are part of your **information body** which is structured, organized or **"formed"** energy **(in-formation).** If you look at the things around you, you realize you can tell a story about each item: where it came from, what memories are associated with it, and what purpose it serves. Think of the last story you heard that made you emotional. What changes in your body when you feel angry? What changes in your body when you feel sad? Have you ever listened to a story that made you sad and noticed tears welling in your eyes? Have you ever listened to a story that made you excited and noticed your heart beating faster? These are examples of how your information body influences your energy body and your physical body.

Now you can celebrate your perfection and **integrate all three bodies**. Just like a flame cannot be separated from the candle of which it is a part, and just like the ocean cannot be separated from its shoreline, your thoughts, emotions, soul, spirit, and vital energy cannot be separated from your body. Ancient Taoists observed that Chi holds our cells and organs together. When a person starts losing their vital energy, their organs often sag down. And of course, every living organism eventually exhausts all their Chi and dies. In death, all elements are decomposed and returned to nature and the original source of Chi. One question you can start asking yourself is whether your choices, actions, and thoughts create more life — or deplete and diminish it.

When your brain receives a balanced stream of stimulation from all three bodies, you feel alive and in flow. You know what your body is doing; you sense your environment, and you are aware when your energy changes. You tell yourself empowering and uplifting stories, and you feel terrific.

Everything is energy, including your sexual desire and your radiant glow. However, this energy needs the hardware of your brain and body neurology. Being human means to have a human body, whether you like it or not. Sadly, this body can be depleted, damaged, aged, and eventually destroyed. But those who know how to preserve, move, and manage their energy have the magic key to aging brilliantly.

Yin and Yang

Have you ever tried to stay positive when something very negative was happening to you? This is what I used to do before I started studying Taoist vitality practices. Unfortunately, this never worked for me. I would spend hours and days and even weeks wrestling with my bad mood, trying to be cheerful and optimistic.

Ancient Taoists noticed that the opposing conditions of heat and cold, expansion and contraction, and heaviness and lightness are essential to the flow of life. They discovered the law of harmony and interaction of opposites: Yin and Yang. Even before discoveries of modern quantum physics, ancient sages wrote that everything is Chi (electromagnetic energy) in its various forms. When Chi becomes condensed, it manifests as material objects and living things. When Chi expands, it becomes light, air, steam, heat, and other forms of immaterial energy. They decided to call the expansive, hot, bright, and light energy which resembles sun, air, and steam "Yang," or masculine energy. They called the dark, dense, and cold energy which resembles water and earth "Yin," or feminine energy. They noticed that both males and females have Yin and Yang energy, and they observed that these two opposite energies have to be in balance to create the flow of life. If there is too much sun, the earth will be dry and barren. If there is too much earth but not enough sun, the flowers won't have enough energy to grow. Yin and Yang engage in the dance of life, playing and moving together, creating and recreating each other.

The Tai Chi symbol representing the Yin and Yang concept.

The concept of Yin and Yang is the essence of all Taoist vitality practices. Every human body has both Yin and Yang energy. Every woman has some Yang and produces the male sex hormone testosterone; every man has some Yin and makes female estrogen. And yet, women are uniquely connected to and replenished by their Yin power.

A woman's body is like earth. Earth is Yin. It has to be nourished and well taken care of, so in the richness of her vitality, her creative and manifesting power can continue to blossom. When earth is depleted, dry, and exhausted, nothing grows. It doesn't mean a woman can't do the things a man does. We all have feminine Yin and masculine Yang energy in us. But a woman's very special, ancient, deep, rich, and fertile power and magic comes from deep, rich, and fertile earth. It flows with water and blossoms with deep roots.

Many women believe that aches, pains, permanent exhaustion, feeling numb, and forgetting the sound of own laugher are just signs of natural aging.

But what if there were another way?

Science and Chi

One thing everyone knows about electricity is it requires a completed connection. If there is a break or an area of resistance in the electrical wiring, the flow of electricity will be interrupted. This is how an electrical off switch works: by disconnecting the wires and stopping the current. Electricity also requires a source – a battery or a generator. This is true for your body as well. All organs have to work as a team to create your river of light. Let's take a look at our vital organs.

Brain
Many people identify themselves with their brain only. Brains believe they are very important, and they command a premium share of all energy produced in the body. Even in a resting state the brain can consume up to 20% of the body's energy. Interestingly enough, **thinking does not require a lot of energy**. When the brain is idle it can produce from 50,000 to 80,000 thoughts each day, which means we can think thousands of thoughts in one hour and dozens of thoughts per second.

Solving a problem or engaging in a creative process involves more structures in the brain, and can be more energy consuming. Emotions use even more energy because they involve the entire body, including muscles and internal organs.

Our brain is like a king. It's important and expensive, but it does not produce enough energy. Every organ's job is to support the brain, but the brain itself is an organ.

It's interesting scientists only recently began talking about human consciousness as a very special form of electromagnetic energy. Biologist and molecular geneticist Johnjoe McFadden at The University of Surrey has proposed the term "CEMI" (Consciousness Electro-Magnetic Information) Fields. Their basis is the electromagnetic activity of our neurons. But what results from this activity — the electromagnetic cloud of structured energy — is actually intelligent. It can be programmed and organized into thoughts, ideas, mental images, and more.

Wow — finally! Even scientists now believe our thoughts are made from real physical energy! When a woman has vibrant and powerful energy on the inside, she radiates allure, sensuality, and beauty all around. This energy is felt as buzzing skin, tingling warmth, and pleasurable vibrations by other human beings. Now we know why.

Lungs

The brain is hidden inside the skull and cannot go outside for a breath of air. So it needs another organ called lungs to breathe. As you breathe in you fill your lungs with oxygen-rich air. Next, oxygen from the air traverses the thin lining of your lungs' alveola. Blood cells contain hemoglobin; red pigment which can be saturated with oxygen. The oxygen-laden blood cells travel through your body with a mission to deliver oxygen to your every cell.

Mitochondria

The reason we need to breathe is because our body uses oxygen to generate electromagnetic energy in structures called mitochondria, producing a chemical compound called ATP (adenosine-triphosphate).

Here's the great thing about ATP: When it converts into another compound, adenosine-di-phosphate (ADP), it releases electromagnetic energy. We are creatures of light and air. We breath air and take in oxygen and we turn it into light — electrical energy — inside our cells. Mitochondria are our power plants and they are located inside every living cell. Some cells, such as those found in the kidneys and heart, are packed with mitochondria. In order to manufacture energy our power plants need fuel, which is provided by our digestive system. If you see how much space inside your body is taken by your digestive system, you will realize how important it is to fuel up your body. You cannot just take a spoonful of soup and feed it to your tiny cells. Food has to be broken down into smaller and smaller particles, until it can be absorbed into the intestinal walls and into the bloodstream.

Heart

Place one hand on your heart and wiggle your toes. Do you feel the thump-thump in your chest? This is your heart pumping blood. It starts working when you are still a fetus inside the uterus, and it stops pumping only when you die. When you wiggle your toes you're proving your toes are alive, and this means they are receiving blood. The heart is a big muscle. It pumps blood into two big blood vessels: your aorta and pulmonary artery. The aorta is a passage for blood, which is delivered to every organ, tissue, and cell in the body. The pulmonary artery carries oxygenated blood from the lungs to the heart. Your cells are very small; so small you can only see them under a powerful microscope. If you tried to feed them from a large blood vessel it would be like watering a tiny flower with a firehose. This is why your blood vessels branch into smaller and smaller vessels, until they become so tiny that blood cells have to squeeze through them in single file. At this stage they are called capillaries, and can also only be seen under a microscope.

When your blood is free of toxins and replenished with adequate hydration, your red blood cells flow through the capillaries with relative ease, especially if they are relaxed and open. But a lack of hydration — and the presence of toxins in your blood — can make your red blood cells form stacks called "rouleaux." If you also have stress constricting your capillaries, it becomes very difficult for your blood to deliver oxygen to (and flush toxins from) your cells. A stagnant, suffocating, and unhealthy environment is created within your body.

As the blood releases oxygen and is saturated with carbon dioxide (CO_2), the blood vessels absorb toxins and waste products from cells and start forming bigger and bigger vessels. They gather into a big vena (vein) which returns blood to and from the heart and the lungs. When CO_2 is not properly released (as when a person holds their breath) toxins accumulate, accelerating aging.

Imagine your heart, which is approximately the size of your fist. It pumps blood through an immense network of blood vessels and tiny capillaries, making sure every organ and cell receive blood. That's a lot of work!

In the past, humans had to move: They walked, ran, worked in the fields, climbed trees, and fought. When you move your body the large muscles in your calves, thighs, and buttocks work like additional hearts to help return blood to the actual heart.

Digestive and eliminating systems

Energy production requires good breathing, digestion, circulation, absorption, and elimination. If a person is anxious, they won't be breathing well and their digestive system won't be at its optimal performance. If a person is also sitting for most of the day, their heart might not be able to circulate blood through all areas of their body. If a person is constantly stressed, their digestion might be suppressed and their metabolism might be more inclined to deposit fat into their abdomen and buttocks, because this is what was needed in the past when things would get tough. Stress and immobility increase inflammation in the body, which in turn impacts the brain and internal organs. Inflammation also negatively impacts skin, causing premature wrinkles and skin deterioration. It is very interesting that many Americans have learned to be afraid of calories in food, because calories are just a measure of how much energy the body can produce from any particular food. Calories are not what we should fear. We should be afraid of living in a way which favors both weight gain and energy depletion at the same time. And the consequences are more serious than just upsetting your body's esthetics. Without energy your cells cannot breathe, move, renew, or regenerate. Without electricity flowing through your body you cannot breathe passion and have the special air that inspires love and desire. It's not the weight gain itself; it's stress, impaired digestion, inflammation, and disrupted energy flow which create health issues, upset moods, and lead to mental and physical exhaustion. When you live in a way which squeezes the living light out of your body without replenishing it, you end up with a body which has lost its vibrancy and vitality.

Aging

The body can age, but energy is ageless. Energy can dissipate or be transformed into other forms of energy, but it does not age. Physical structures age and deteriorate, but energy can be replenished, renewed, and regenerated. We are vibrational beings, and this means our energy is everything. We are like lanterns shining our light. Sometimes our light is diminished. Sometimes we forget how to shine. Being ageless means having a vibrant spirit illuminating your body, and a mindset making it easy to take daily actions designed to help keep your body young, healthy, and agile. It is maintaining the inner state which supports regeneration, renewal, healing, and personal growth.

Let's Do It!

Nature is medicine, and it's easily available for no charge. We just need to remember to take it daily. I take my nature medicine by breathing with intention. It's not difficult to learn, and takes minutes to do.

Imagine a tranquil and serene body of water.

Notice the color blue.

Imagine being immersed in this blue energy.

Imagine standing on the shore of a beach. Feel the earth beneath your feet.

Let your skin feel the light breeze, and maybe even the warm kisses of sunshine.

Notice how more and more blue space seems to open up in front of you.

Close your eyes and inhale the fresh cool air.

Focus in on the song of a bird, or the laughter of children.

Open your eyes, and let your heart open up to the blue space in front of you. Notice how much blue energy is available to you.

Blue, calm, tranquil, and flowing.

Breathe in…blue.

Breathe out and release dark, heavy, and cloudy energy.

Breathe in…calm.

Breathe out and release stress and tension. Be at peace.

Open a healing space in your heart and fill it with blue energy. Breathe in…more blue.

Fill yourself with blue. Fill yourself with tranquility and flow. As you cool your heart with tranquil blue light, feel at peace.

You are safe right here and now. You are loved. All is well in the moment.

And as you go through your day, feel the healing presence of nature in your heart.

Chapter 4

Estrogens and Sexual Energy – Misunderstood and Mismanaged

To be a woman and have a biologically female body means that your body is producing estrogens, and is affected by these compounds. Estrogens are a collective name for a group of female sexual hormones which include estradiol, the most abundant hormone in women of childbearing age; estriol, the main estrogen during pregnancy; and estrone, the only estrogen a woman's body still makes after menopause. Even though men also have estrogens and are also affected by these compounds, they do not have to deal with the monthly fluctuations of estrogens. They do not get pregnant, and they do not have to go through menopause and experience a sudden hormonal shift affecting their entire body.

It is surprising how many women — and how many doctors — view estrogens as something only needed for sex and reproduction. Just because estrogens regulate sex and reproduction doesn't mean they do nothing else. A hormone is a compound which regulates cellular metabolism by binding with special structures on the cellular membrane called receptors. Each hormone has its own receptor. Each hormone fits its receptor like a key fits the lock for which it is designed. Estrogens bind to estrogen receptors. The effect will be different depending on where the estrogen receptors are located, and which biological process they activate.

You can visualize receptors as switches. You have the switch, and you have the wiring, and you have the device which is activated by the switch — but none of this will work until something activates the switch. Receptors can also be compared to a keyhole or a security code on a door. Not just anyone can open the door. It has to be someone who knows the code. Estrogens know the security code, and can open the door. This, by the way, is also the reason estrogens can potentially stimulate cancerous growth. It is not because they are evil; it is simply because some tumors have estrogen receptors, and are controlled by them.

Estrogen receptors are found in the reproductive organs, but also in skin, bones, fat, connective tissues, muscles, and the brain. In menopause, when estrogen levels drops, all these organs will feel the effect.

Skin

Estrogen participates in the synthesis of collagen. Therefore, when estrogens diminish during menopause, skin aging becomes more noticeable and progresses faster. Women also might notice more facial hair, uneven pigmentation, and changes in fat distribution. Skin aging is more noticeable in areas which are exposed to sunlight, and often accumulate sun-induced damage: the face, neck, décolleté, forearms, and back of the hands. It is important to know that skin, and especially subcutaneous fat, can produce estrogens, and partially support the body through menopause. Therefore, taking good care of one's own skin — and not minding the gain of a few extra pounds during the transition phase — can make menopause much more bearable.

Bone and Muscle Health

In both men and women, estrogens are required for bone metabolism. Testosterone, the male sexual hormone, helps build stronger bones and muscles; estrogen improves bone density, and reduces inflammation in muscles. Consequently, during menopause, many women experience bone fragility. They are often surprised that falls, which in the past would have had no consequences, can now result in fractures. They might also be surprised they have more aches and pains after an intense workout. It has been established that premenopausal women who were treated with estrogen suppressors in an attempt to slow down ovarian cancer experienced severely deteriorated bone microstructure.

Estrogen decline might cause changes in the pelvic bones, connective tissues, and muscle, increasing the risk of pelvic organ prolapse. This is a condition so common in menopausal women that some experts call it a hidden epidemic. As the pelvic bones slowly dissolve and become weaker, it becomes more difficult for the connective tissues and muscles of the pelvic floor to keep the pelvic organs uplifted. Since muscles and connective tissues are also affected, the whole structure begins to sag, with the bladder, vagina, and uterus shifting down. Pelvic organ prolapse often requires surgery — which has a 38% relapse rate, and needs to be repeated.

Heart
Since the heart is a muscle, it is affected by estrogen decline in menopause.

Cognitive Decline
Brain cells have estrogen receptors, and need estrogen to function. Loss of estrogen is linked to various mental effects ranging from "brain fog" and mood swings to memory loss and an elevated risk of Alzheimer's disease.

Urogenital Aging
Vaginal dystrophia (progressive thinning of the vaginal walls), vaginal prolapse (sagging of the vagina through the pelvic floor), urinary incontinence, painful intercourse, and vaginal dryness – these are all just some of the very unpleasant and disturbing conditions which might develop in menopause.

Visceral Fat
Estrogens affect the distribution of fat. In addition to developing a thicker padding under the skin, there is an accumulation of visceral fat, which is fat in the abdominal cavity around the internal organs. This fat might impede the mobility of organs, and negatively impact digestion and other vital functions.

Tiredness and Physical Exhaustion

A 2021 study published in the Journal of Menopausal Medicine studied the health complaints of menopausal women in the rural areas of Uttar Pradesh, India. Researchers interviewed women ranging from 45 to 55 years of age, with a total of 315 women participating in the study. The most frequent complaints among the participants were of feeling tired and worn out (85.1%), and of muscle and joint pain (67.6%). The authors noted that in rural India women are much less likely to see a doctor about their feminine complaints, and are much less likely to discuss these issues with other people. In this study, over 50% of the participants were illiterate, and 58% were housewives. The social stigma and shame attached to the female reproductive system made it very difficult for these women to get qualified help.

Unfortunately, this is also often true for urban-dwelling, affluent, and educated American women — only for a different reason. A majority of educated, successful, and ambitious American women believe they should not show any weakness which might be attributed to their feminine biology. So they grit their teeth, and silently push through their discomfort as if admitting they are humans affected by the physiological changes in their aging bodies is a sign of weakness. Sadly, this often prevents them from taking the appropriate steps to alleviate and prevent these changes.

If we apply the metaphor "women are like earth," it will become clear that no amount of positive thinking and willpower can change the fact that depleted soil needs remedial measures before it can produce beautiful flowers. It is not enough to do something; it is paramount to do the *right* thing. The delicate condition of the menopausal feminine body doesn't need forceful masculine tactics. It requires intelligence, compassion, patience, kindness, and daily care.

Taoist masters developed practices for supporting the pelvic organs and other organs in the female body by improving circulation; keeping the internal environment cleaner by ensuring good lymph flow; and nourishing the body with feminine sexual energy. They discovered that the slow, mindful, and graceful movements of Qigong are gentler on the muscles. They do not cause strain, damage, and inflammation; in fact, they help stimulate circulation, detox tissues, bring more water to connective tissues, and strengthen the bones. They also discovered that mental imagery and mindfulness associated with Qigong and Taoist meditations help keep the brain active, and slow down cognitive decline. While forceful masculine workouts may put unnecessary strain on the heart muscle, gentle Qigong helps lessen the heart's workload by turning body muscles into "additional hearts" which delegate some of the circulation duties to them. Taoist ageless technology combines physical practices with mental and spiritual practices to create an integrative uplift to support the mind, body, and spirit, and turn menopause into a sacred feminine journey.

Sexual Energy is Magic

Let's travel back to the time in your personal history when a tiny sperm made it all the way to the prize: a love union with an egg.

Have you ever heard the expression "a million-to-one chance?" Consider this: A healthy man can ejaculate 200–500 million sperm in one shot! Only one sperm (in rare cases two or more) makes it to the egg. For one sperm, the path to becoming a human being lies through millions of dead comrades. This one lucky sperm, charged with love and orgasmic energy and pulled by a massive charge of the primordial force of cosmic energy, began its journey as a human being. Talk about a Big Bang! A new Universe was created. You were born. A million-to-one chance is nothing compare to winning this incredible cosmic lottery: being conceived and born.

According to the Taoist teachings, when we are conceived we receive 100% of our life force.

This life force is divided into three parts.

1. Principal life force: 50% of your life force is yours to use throughout your lifetime.
2. The emergency reserve: 25% is yours to use only when you need an extra boost (if you are sick, wounded, or chased by a lion).
3. Sexual energy: 25% is reserved to ensure you procreate and leave your genetic copies to continue your bloodline.

According to the Tao, some people are born with abundant principal energy, while others might be given a more limited supply. It's like winning a cosmic lottery. The same 100% of principal life force (which is 50% of life force) can be enough for some people to live recklessly and abuse their bodies in many ways. Some people can win big and spend lavishly all their lives; others have limited wins and risk to spend it too quickly. The key is to take what you have and use it wisely. Just because you were gifted with abundant energy doesn't mean it's wise to live your life burning through your good fortune. And just because you were born with smaller energy reserves doesn't mean you have to age fast and die young. It's all about being energy savvy.

According to the Tao, 25% of your reserve energy is stored in your kidneys.

This energy is for emergencies only. When you are in mortal danger or when you are sick, this energy is used to help you stay alive and get back to health. We can also trick the kidneys into releasing this energy just by thinking anxiously about an incoming deadline, or by having a cup of coffee. Modern science confirms that stressful and frightening events trigger the release of adrenaline from adrenal glands, located on top of the kidneys. The Taoist masters discovered this long ago. Adrenaline helps mobilize energy, and increases the ability for fight or flight. Stress is an important and healthy reaction. But so many women use stress to burn their energy reserves. Their body is left unprotected in case of an injury or illness.

Many women believe being constantly stressed helps them deal with problems. But problems never end! And if they never return the energy they borrow, more stress just leads to more depletion and exhaustion. Being constantly "wired and tired" depletes your life force. The more you learn to relax and feel good, the more energy you have in reserve to get you through tough life challenges such as major illness, loss, and adversity. This energy is also used more as we age, because our body needs more energy to repair and regenerate. Age is not just a number. You have to remember to reserve enough power to regenerate and rejuvenate, because your body starts breaking more.

Finally, 25% of your energy is stored in your sexual organs as your reproductive sexual energy, or "Jing Chi."

It takes a lot of life force to grow a human being in your body. Since procreation is so important, nature made sure you have enough energy to have a baby every year. Every month some of this energy is lost through menstruation. Some of this energy is used to grow and breastfeed a baby or a few babies. In modern life, most women limit themselves to having one to three children. Even if they have five or six kids, that's still much less than nature intended for you. This means even in menopause your body still has plenty of sexual energy in reserve. The Taoists believed we could channel this energy to become our life force. Without exhausting our sexual powers, we can use them to have more clarity in our thinking, more sparkle in our eyes, more lift in our skin, and more fire in our belly.

The Yoni Egg Practice

Taoists believed they could turn sexual energy into spiritual energy, and knew how to keep their sexual organs alive and vital. Sexual practices for women included using a beautifully carved Jade egg to train a woman's yoni to be strong and vibrant. In the past, Jade egg practices were kept secret. Today, we can enjoy and use these practices thanks to Taoist masters who preserved and carried them on. Today, women use these practices to stay healthy, strong, and vibrant with strong, healthy, and vibrant yoni.

Your sexual organs are capable of generating powerful energy. Usually you let other people activate their flow. This time you are going to be in charge. You are going to help your yoni become tight, strong, and vibrant so it can give you power, confidence, and strength. The eggs originally used by Taoist women were made of Jade. These days many kinds of beautiful gemstones are used to make Yoni eggs. Any woman can learn the Yoni egg practice, and benefit from it.

If you feel uncomfortable thinking about putting a stone egg into your vagina, you are feeling the effects of centuries of negative social and cultural conditioning. Let's put it this way: If you wanted to take a woman's power away, how would you go about it? One way is to make her feel it is not okay to use it, or to cultivate it. Think of the life force in your body as a mighty river. If you want your whole body to be nourished by this river, you want to make sure there are no stagnant areas. If you want your river to be powerful, why would you disconnect and deplete the most powerful source of the flow? When women reconnect to their feminine force, they reconnect to their magic, power, and confidence. They start looking younger, more radiant, and more vital.

Women are like earth. Sexual energy is like water. Open the flow. You deserve the luxury of deciding how you want to spend your older years. Whether you want to have hot steamy sex at the age of 80, or just want to radiate your beauty and breathe passion into your every endeavor — the choice is yours.

The Yoni egg practice is a physical practice to bring more energy, flow, and awareness to your sexual organs. It only takes five minutes a day to receive all the benefits, and requires only a drilled stone egg strung with a piece of floss.

Sexual energy is very powerful. It's so powerful it can easily sweep away your reason. You want to turn it into a clean and nourishing river, which flows gently and powerfully through your body, bringing vitality and power to your organs and your soul. Taoists believed the sexual energy activation was the true secret of beauty and radiance. When your sexual energy is flowing and moving, your skin glows and you radiate alluring vibes. However, before you activate your sexual energy you have to do a lot of energy clearing.

A Little Bonsai Tree

Once upon a time there was a little tree, which was boldly grasping the earth with its tiny roots. It was basking in sunshine and pulling nutrients and water from the soil because it knew it would grow and become a big, beautiful, and magnificent tree. One day, a man came with a shovel and dug the little tree from the earth to put it in a big flower pot. At first, the pot seemed awfully small and uncomfortable. But people would come and trim and tame growing branches, shaping them into shapes which they believed were beautiful and fancy. Year after year went by. Eventually, the little tree forgot all about its old life and was quite happy growing in a pot and having people compliment and admire its beauty. Only sometimes at night, the little bonsai tree had strange dreams in which its branches were reaching the sky and its roots were spreading deep into the earth. "What a weird dream I just had!" thought the little bonsai tree and did its best to forget all about it.

Let's Do This!

The next time you undress in the bathroom, stand naked in front of the mirror and look at yourself.

How do you feel?

If you feel confident, proud, and happy in your body, smile at yourself and celebrate your beauty.

If you feel awkward, uncomfortable, and ashamed, smile at yourself and give yourself a hug. Promise you will help that woman in the mirror feel like a goddess in her body. (If you prefer a witch or a queen, feel free to use that!)

What would you like to teach a younger you about her body if you had a chance? What would you like to teach every little girl if you had a chance? Write it down.

Congratulate yourself and celebrate your beauty.

Ask yourself:

1. Do I get enough sleep?
   If yes, celebrate yourself. If no, smile at yourself and start setting up the intention for self-care.
2. Do I allow myself time to sit down and savor my food? Do I take time to nourish my body?
   If yes, give yourself a high-five and congratulate yourself. If you always eat on the go while doing a million tasks, smile at yourself and start setting up the intention for mindful nourishment.
3. Do I give myself time to rest and regenerate when I am tired, unwell, or injured?
   If yes, give yourself an A+. If no, give yourself an A+ for making the decision to make positive changes.

Chapter 5

The Inner Smile:
A 5,000-Year-Old Healing Tool

A Taoist Master asked a student, "How you can make your enemy very happy?"

The student didn't know the answer.

"You get really angry. And you keep all this anger inside. And you get sick, have a heart attack, and end up in a hospital. And your enemy is very happy."

Then he asked, "How you can make your enemy very unhappy?"

This time, the student knew the answer.

"I go on with my life, and stay happy, and let go of all anger, and my enemy gets angrier and angrier, and finally gets sick, and ends up in a hospital."

I first heard this story from Master Chia. I remember a day when I truly understood this teaching.

It was a crisp spring morning. I looked out the window and discovered a pile of assorted garbage on my lawn. There were wrappers, milk cartons, and other remnants of human activity.

What? Who left that here? Who's is going to clean it up?

I knew the answer to the last question. Whoever left this garbage was not going to clean it up. That was going to be my job.

I could sit there and build theories and muse and rack my brain trying to find out what happened. Or I could just clean it up. Which I did.

This nicely sums up the Taoist approach to psychology.

While Western psychology was developing "talk therapy" based on listening and analyzing patients' stories and labeling their conditions, Taoists focused on the three bodies: the physical, energy, and information fields. They believed information is tricky because it activates the energy connected to it. They said, "Let's just focus on clearing toxic energy. Who cares why it's there? Let's just clear it out."

If you think about your cells, tissues, and organs as your pristine lush green lawn, what are the emotions that feel, sound, and look like unsightly toxic garbage?

Which emotions uplift and rejuvenate you?

Which emotions pollute your body and drain your energy?

Resist the temptation to label or judge them. Just smile into them and notice the qualities. What feels draining and toxic? If you imagine your body filled with sensual, vital, beautiful, rich, fresh, harmonious energy, what could diminish your vibrancy? I invite you to start thinking about your negative emotions as garbage.

Hear me out. I am not saying your emotions are garbage. I simply invite you to start questioning the need to hold pain in your body after it has served its purpose.

Think about items you've thrown into your garbage can lately. Maybe it was a food item accidentally left rotting in the back of the fridge. It doesn't make the item bad. It just means it served its purpose, and is no longer nutritious or safe to consume. Adopt the same attitude toward the negative emotions you're holding in your body now. Most of them are expired. Some of them are quite rotten, and should have been thrown away many years ago.

"Revenge is a dish best served cold." You've heard that saying. Revenge also poisons the heart of the person who keeps consuming it. People harboring revenge plans and holding on to resentment are often so depleted and destroyed by decades of holding a grudge, they are surprised to discover the act of revenge fails to make them as happy as they hoped. It often leaves them sad, empty, and devastated. Revenge is a cold, poisonous dish you have to eat yourself.

Every piece of garbage starts as something we use. It can be a wrapper for a gift, or a cake. It can be peelings from potatoes. It can be a milk cartoon.

Negative emotions are not bad or wrong. They are useful and important. In Taoist traditions, negative emotions are Yin – they are denser, heavier, and colder, and they have the same energy as earth. Therefore they can be returned to earth. Even though they are not bad, they can accumulate in the body and obstruct the flow of life. They create inner blockages and heavy, inflexible armor, which might seem protective but can in fact prevent good things from flowing into our life. Positive emotions are Yang – they are brighter, lighter, expanding, uplifting, and empowering. However, they might burn out quickly if there is not enough fuel. Therefore enthusiasm, passion, and excitement usually cannot stay in the body indefinitely. According to the Tao, true happiness is created by a balanced flow of positive and negative emotions forming the river of life. We do not have to always be positive. But we need to be aware of the danger of being stuck in negativity. If we keep negative emotions in our body without releasing them, they might start rotting and damaging our tissues. They also might block the flow of energy, and create stagnant areas which are easily affected by diseases. They feel heavy and dark, and they make it difficult to become excited, motivated, and uplifted. With time, they might suck all the joy out of life, and all the vitality and vibrancy out of the body.

Who cares where they came from? Who cares who angered me, or what my ex said to me 30 years ago, or how much criticism I had to endure from my father? If it feels toxic, clear it out. Whoever left these negative, toxic, and painful emotions on the fresh green lawn of my soul, mind, and body, is not going to clean it up. I might as well do it myself. I think in my case it was a bear who left that garbage on my lawn. I thought about being resentful and spending the next 10 years of my life trying to convince this bear to apologize and clean up. But I decided to just clean it up myself.

Relax, Release and Let Go

It requires a lot of energy to hold on to old pain and grudges. The body has to create an energy vault to keep all this rotten stinky emotional garbage separated from the rest of the body. The older we get, the more pain lockers we need to build to keep all the toxic emotional energy in.

This blocks our vitality, poisons the well of our passion, puts more wrinkles on our face, creates tension and inflammation in our body, and extinguishes our fire.

Sir David Hawkins wrote the book *Power vs Force*. In this book, he talks about a study which examined the energetic effects of various emotions on our physical body. Emotions measuring above 200 made the body stronger, while emotions measuring below 200 drained the body and made it weaker.

Love measured 500. Bliss was 600. And enlightenment states were above 700. Shame measured at 20!

One of the reasons women often do not realize their own power is because women historically have been conditioned to be afraid, ashamed, and preferably ignorant of their sexuality. It's time to reclaim our magic.

Women's bodies are like earth. Their feminine energy is like water. Without water nothing grows. If you want to awaken your feminine vitality, you must feed your body joy and love — and let go of shame.

Taoists believed that a human being lives to experience the full range of emotions. They are like a symphony which makes our life rich and colorful. According to the Tao, it's unrealistic to expect you will never be angry or sad. To expect a human being will never feel angry, sad, frustrated, or annoyed is like expecting your house or backyard will never require cleaning. Even very neat and organized people need to clean their house from time to time. It's the same with emotions. In fact, life would be sad, brutal, and short without negative emotions. They are messengers which keep us safe and tell us, "Hey, get out of here. It's not safe and not fun."

Taoists developed many practices for cleaning toxic emotional energy from our body. They have a simple concept which I like a lot: "Clean the cells and organs, and let the body heal itself."

Sometimes the best thing we can do to reignite our passion is to just do a big spring cleaning.

Let's Do This!

1. Find a comfortable position. Take a deep breath and let it out slowly. Relax into your body.

2. Imagine a beautiful cloud of golden light is right in front of you. You can see it, you can just think about it, or intuit that it is there. Use whatever magic of imagination feels right for you.

3. Now, think for a moment of how negative energy manifests itself in your body. Is it heavy? Dark? Cloudy? Chaotic and muddy? Gray? Itchy? Tense? Any way you experience toxic and negative energy in your body is fine. Accept it, and resist the temptation to block, judge, or analyze it. Just let it be. Move it to the back of your thinking for now.

4. Go back to the golden light. Take a long, deep breath, and inhale the golden light. Hold it in your body for a moment and imagine it mixing with the negative energy. As you exhale, imagine exhaling and releasing all the dark and negative energy, and allowing it to be absorbed into earth.

5. Repeat nine times, each time inhaling the golden light, and releasing any manifestation of negative energy into the ground.

6. Imagine the golden light entering your forehead on the exhale and washing through your spine all the way to the tailbone.

7. Stand up and shake your body. Feel the flow of energy buzzing through your veins and every fiber of your being.

The Inner Smile

If you grew up in a family where a display of emotions was not welcome, you might have learned how to hide your feelings and smile even when you are hurt, angry, or depressed. Ancient Taoist masters believed we can use a loving smile not to hide or mask our feelings, but to release negative emotional energy and replenish loving energy in our own body.

The magic of a loving smile.

Think about it. What do you do when you want to connect with somebody? You smile. What do you do when you want to show somebody you love them? You smile. Think of your smile as smiling sunshine, shining on your own organs to uplift them and warm them up. Let's begin to learn this beautiful ancient meditation. I learned it from Master Chia, and fell in love with it immediately. So simple. And so powerful. According to Taoist wisdom, you direct and move energy with your eyes, heart, and mind. All you need to do is to relax and smile. When you are tense and negative, you cannot move your energy. The Inner Smile starts with the eyes, then goes to the heart, and then follows the Five Elements Creating Cycle discovered by the Taoists.

Five elements in the body.

Let's Do This!

1. Find a comfortable position with your feet planted into the floor. Take a few deep relaxing breaths and relax your shoulders.

2. Gently rock your spine to release tension.

3. Find a spot on the wall and focus your attention on it.

4. Imagine you are looking at something very important. Imagine pouring your mind essence into this spot. This is the outward focus. This is what you do when you are engaged with your phone, or listening to someone talking. Notice the energy flowing out of your body.

5. Take a deep breath, relax, and think of someone you love. Imagine this person standing right in front of you. You can also imagine your dog (if you have a dog) or a beautiful place in nature.

6. When you feel loving energy activating in your heart, simply smile as you would when you feel love. Lift up the corners of your mouth and notice how it feels.

7. Still smiling, take another deep breath, relax and smile into your own eyes. Feel your eyes softening and relaxing.

8. Next, place your hands over your heart, look into your heart, and smile into your heart. Think, "Thank you, heart! I love you!'

9. Keep smiling into your heart, pouring love and gratitude into it, until your heart starts smiling at you.

The Five Elements Creating Cycle

Heart is **fire** and the color **red**. It is nourished by the positive emotions of **love, joy, and happiness**. When the heart holds the negative energy of *hate, judgement, cruelty, arrogance, impatience, resentment, and guilt*, the fire becomes destructive.

Loving **fire** in the heart helps to replenish **earth**.

Spleen is **earth** and the color **yellow**. It is nourished by the positive energies of **trust, faith, and confidence**. Earth has a grounding and supporting energy. Negative emotions of the spleen are *doubt, worry, and anxiety*.

When **earth** is growing and abundant, it gives birth to **metal**.

Lungs are **metal** and the color **white.** Lungs are nourished by **courage and righteous feelings.** Negative energies of the lungs are *sadness, depression, and grief.*

When the lungs are nourished by courage, **metal** attracts **water.**

Kidneys are **water** and the color **blue.** Kidneys are nourished by **calmness, tranquility, and peace.** The negative energy of kidneys are *fear and stress.*

When kidneys are nourished by calmness, **water** helps grow the forest — the source of **wood.**

Liver is **wood** and the color **green.** Liver is nurtured by **kindness and generosity.** The liver is negatively affected by *greediness, jealousy, anger, and shame.*

In the Five Elements Creating Cycle you smile into each organ, imagining vibrant and clear colors representing nourishing emotions. Dark and cloudy colors represent toxic and negative emotional energy.

Organ	Nature Element	Color	Positive Energy	Negative Energy
Heart, small intestine	Fire	Red	Love, joy, happiness	Hate, arrogance, impatience, rage, cruelty
Spleen, pancreas, stomach	Earth	Yellow	Trust, confidence, faith	Mistrust, doubts, anxiety, worry
Lungs, large intestine	Metal	White	Courage, openness, fairness	Grief, sadness, depression
Kidneys, Bladder	Water	Blue	Calmness, tranquility, gentleness	Fear, trauma
Liver, gallbladder	Wood	Green	Kindness, generosity	Greed, jealousy, anger, stress, guilt

Remember your goal is not to eliminate all negative emotions; just to prevent the accumulation of emotions which have served their purpose and can be safely released.

Don't do the Inner Smile meditation when you are being chased by a lion. Make sure you are safe, and nothing in your immediate surroundings is threatening to kill you.

Now get comfortable. You can record this meditation on your phone and listen to it, or just memorize the steps and do it. Eventually you can become creative and design your own version of the Inner Smile.

Let's Do This!

Take a deep breath and just relax. Allow your eyes to close. With every breath, relax deeper. Make your eyes soft, cool, and relaxed. Smile into your eyes. Let the smiling energy lift the corners of your mouth. Feel your smiling energy as loving sunshine. Look into your heart and smile into it. See your heart as a loving fire with a red core wrapped in green light. Look into your heart and bring your loving smiling attention into your heart. Imagine your heart opening like a red rose. Smile and breathe into your heart. Feel your heart smiling at you. Relax into your heart. Smile love into your heart. Thank your heart for everything it does for you. "Thank you, heart. I love you."

If you have any cruelty, hatred, judgement, or impatience in your heart, smile at them and shine your sunshine on them until they melt. Imagine all the negative energy melting and flowing down into the earth. Let the golden light of Mother Earth energy replenish fire in your heart.

Smile into your belly and connect with your small intestine. Let loving fire energy flow from your heart into your small intestine. Let it radiate love into your spleen and pancreas.

Imagine your spleen filled with yellow light. Feel earth energy in your spleen. Stable, grounding, and solid. Smile into your spleen until your spleen starts smiling at you. Think of trust, confidence, and faith. Say, "Thank you, spleen. I love you, spleen." If you have any worry, anxiety, or doubts in your spleen, smile at them and shine your sunshine on them until they melt. Imagine all the negative energy melting and flowing down into the earth. Let the golden light of Mother Earth energy replenish earth in your spleen.

Smile into your stomach and fill it with earth energy. Let the light radiate into your lungs.

Look into your lungs. Smile into your lungs. Fill your lungs with white light. Feel courage in your lungs as metal energy. See your lungs smiling at you. Say, "Thank you, lungs! I love you, lungs."

If you have any sadness or grief in your lungs, smile at them and shine your sunshine on them until they melt. Imagine all the negative energy melting and flowing down into the earth. Let the golden light of Mother Earth energy replenish metal energy in your lungs.

Let the white light flow into your large intestine, and smile into your large intestine.

Allow the light to radiate into your kidneys. Feel water energy in your kidneys. Smile into your kidneys. Imagine a tranquil blue lake or a gently rolling river. Say, "Thank you, kidneys. I love you, kidneys." If you have any fear or stress in your kidneys, smile at them and shine your sunshine on them until they melt. Imagine all the negative energy melting and flowing down into the earth. Let the golden light of Mother Earth energy replenish water in your kidneys.

Say, "I release all negativity into the earth and I exchange it for the golden light. I am abundant. I am safe. I am peaceful. I am calm. Calmness is my superpower. I flow like a river."

Smile into your bladder and sexual organs. Smile into your breasts. Smile sunshine and melt all the negativity.

Smile into your liver and feel the green energy of the forest as kindness and generosity. If you detect any shame or anger, smile into them and melt them like blocks of ice. Imagine all the negative energy melting and flowing down into the earth. Let the golden light of Mother Earth energy replenish green wood energy in your liver.

Go back to your heart and smile into your heart. Imagine feeding your loving fire with green wood energy. Let your earth grow in your spleen, and feel your yellow light growing stronger. Feel more grounded and stable. Stand your ground. Let the earth in your spleen create more metal in your lungs. Let the white light grow stronger. Let the metal in your lungs create more water in your kidneys and let the blue light grow stronger. Send more love to your breasts and yoni. Let water grow more forest in your liver and let the forest feed your loving fire.

Repeat the cycle three, six, or nine times.

Imagine radiating love from your heart to the people you love, your friends and family, and anyone to whom you want to send your healing light.

As you go deeper into the Inner Smile practice, you will see more radiance and glow, and an uplifted youthful expression. You might start developing a deeper appreciation for your body, improved confidence, and self-esteem.

The Inner Smile for Harmonious Relationships

To love is to understand. And in order to understand, we need to be able to truly feel without judgement.

In order to do this, we need to be able to identify our own energy which is generated in our own physical body. Our energy might be activated by another person, but it is still our own energy and we are responsible for it. And it is distinctly different from another person's energy, which is generated in *their* physical body. Another person's energy might be activated by us, but it is still their energy and they are responsible for it. We need to be able to distinguish between these separate energies.

In order to do this we need to be able to sit quietly with ourselves - our own body and our own energy - and attend to it mindfully. No matter how deeply we are involved with another person, it is essential to spend some time every day connecting with our own body without giving in to the temptation to justify, judge, or interpret what we experience. It's not in our nature to sit with our own self in peace. So often we immediately start judging, justifying, and interpreting what we feel and think. In all spiritual disciplines, there are meditative practices which train the mind to observe and experience without falling into a rabbit hole of inner conflict. This is exactly what is accomplished through the practice of the Inner Smile. What better way to connect to one's own self than through a loving smile and the energy of unconditional love? The more you learn to feel without resentment, defensiveness, or any other forms of resistance, the more you are able to realize the true nature and qualities of your own energy.

When you smile and feel love, your body releases endorphins, oxytocin, serotonin, and dopamine. These molecules open your skin capillaries, reduce inflammation, stimulate regeneration, and create a radiant glow. Your organs start recognizing they belong to the same body, and learn to support and nourish each other. As you include your yoni (vagina), ovaries, uterus and breasts in this creating cycle of love, you send happy neurochemicals, electromagnetic energy, oxygen, and blood to your female organs. They, in turn, will generate abundant radiant energy for you.

What should you do if you no longer have a uterus, or ovaries, or have had a mastectomy? You can smile into the energy space and imagine your organs made of light.

If you find it difficult to imagine your organs, this is a good time to brush up on your anatomy knowledge. Find a YouTube video and familiarize yourself with your major organs: their shape, location, and essential functions.

Connecting to Your Cosmic Self

Our culture so readily offers material goods as a solution for emotional problems. It's so easy to forget you are not your wrinkles, and you are not your extra pounds. You are not your everyday stress and overwhelm. There is a boundless human spirit living inside of you.

Remember the Taoist concept of our three bodies?

You have your physical body. And your energy body. And your information body, which so often takes over and obscures everything else.

When you start living within the confines of the negative messages coming to you from your screens, social media, and old stories, it's easy to start shrinking. You lose your confidence and divine light.

The Taoist Inner Smile meditation can help change this. Let's review a beautiful variation of this meditation called the Cosmic Inner Smile. When you do it, you expand your energy and your information body well beyond the confines of your physical body; beyond your personal and cultural limitations. You become unlimited.

The original version of this meditation was taught to me by Master Chia. I have modified it for women.

Let's Do This!

Make your eyes heavy and relaxed, and tap your crown. Imagine there is a little antenna extending out of your crown, connecting you to the Universe. Imagine, somewhere in the Universe, there is a source of pure unconditional love. Smile into this cosmic love and feel connection.

With every breath, gently guide this loving energy into your crown, and from your crown down into your heart. Notice the Universe has an inexhaustible supply of love. You will never run out of love.

Smile into your heart and imagine your heart as a cauldron you can fill with love.

Notice your heart is overflowing with love as it starts flowing into your spleen. Smile into your spleen. Smile into the Universe. Guide more love from the Universe into your heart. Let it flow into your small intestine and your spleen. Let it flow from your spleen into your stomach. Let it radiate into your lungs.

Smile into the source of cosmic love. Feel more love flowing through your crown, into your heart, into your small intestine, into your spleen, stomach, and lungs. Breathe love into your skin and let it radiate through your skin.

Smile into the source of universal love. Smile into the moon and the planet and the stars. Feel yourself expanded and connected, filled with love and light.

Let love flow into your large intestine, and then into your kidneys. Keep returning to the cosmic love and guide more love into your crown. Say, "I'm unlimited. I'm loved."

Let love flow into your ovaries and sexual organs. Wrap love around your pelvis.

Guide love into your liver, and from your liver, and back into your heart.

Be still and let the universal love flow through your body, making all your organs glow and smile, feeling loved.

Wiggle your toes and smile from your toes all the way up until your smile blossoms on your lips and illuminates your face.

This simple version of the Cosmic Inner Smile creates a wonderful, expanded state of mind. You feel your vibrations are instantly elevated. You become more grounded in your body, and more connected to your authentic self.

Chapter 6

Becoming Peaceful: Releasing Toxic Anger

"I don't get angry...I grow a tumor instead."
~Alvy Singer, Woody Allen's character from the movie Manhattan

If you are comfortable with expressing your feelings and know how to release anger safely, congratulations! This is a life-saving emotional skill. However, if you have a habit of holding onto your anger while keeping it boiling in your body, you might grow so accustomed to it that you fail to notice when it becomes too big to control. Then you might let this anger take over and turn you into a fire-breathing dragon. You might be dumping this highly toxic and damaging energy on your children or your partner. You might get into an angry fit at work, and it might cost you employment. It might destroy your health and your beauty. And the aftermath might be guilt and remorse, but they do not erase the consequences. When you learn to deal with your anger you make it easier for yourself to recognize and control it without causing energy blockages and explosions.

Toxic Anger

Imagine a lovely autumn morning. I was walking holding my mother's hand, listening to the gentle rustling of red, yellow, and brown leaves under my feet. The air smelled crisp and frosty. I felt elated and exited. I was going to attend a new school, and my mother told me I would love it. I remember instantly falling in love with old trees and an old building. When we walked through the doors, I sniffed the air. Yes, there was this distinct "old building smell," like you sometimes can find in museums and libraries.

This was the last memory I could ever recall before the next one. I am face down on the floor. Another girl is sitting on top of me, pulling my hair, punching and kicking in a frenzy of rage. My face is pressed into a pool of tears. I am terrified. No matter how many times I tried to recall the rest of that morning and the rest of that day, my mind kept jumping straight to that evening.

Fear and anger are basic human emotions we inherited from our furry ancestors. Fear keeps us alive by redirecting energy flow to our arms and legs so we can flee any danger. Anger makes the body stronger physically, enabling it to burn its way through fear and hesitation. Therefore, fear often leads to anger. If you have to defend your children from a hungry lion, this red-hot anger can turn you into someone dangerous enough to make the predator back up and reconsider its dinner plans. Yet, when out of control — and especially when aimed at people you love and care about — it can be very destructive and dangerous. Nothing ages people faster than persistent and deeply held anger. And few things are as deeply traumatic to a child's mind and soul as verbal and/or physical abuse. We rarely have to run away from a tiger. But our mind can easily trick us into believing that our ideas, our rules, and our ego need defending. When it happens, it is very easy to fall into an anger trap and lash out in rage.

Today, scientists confirm that a complex trauma resulting from repeated interpersonal violence in childhood leads to more severe and lasting mental problems in adulthood (compared to simple trauma such as a car accident or any other single traumatic event). Repeated adverse experiences of the same kind become imprinted into our body – not only psychologically, but neurologically, chemically and physiologically. Psychologically and intellectually we can wrap our ideas, beliefs, and understanding around our feelings to create a resemblance of logical and sane behavior. On the physical level of imprinted memories, there is no logic. It is what it is. They are energy codes which open the doors to our emotional reactions.

A lot of physical abuse in childhood stems from uncontrollable parental anger. I was lucky to grow up in a family in which physical abuse was unacceptable. This is why that first attack I experienced in the boarding school terrified me to such a degree. However, it took me a long time to realize that verbal insults (even without physical violence) can also leave very deep scars.

When I transferred from a boarding school to a regular school, I already was a "problem" child. I was rebellious, insubordinate, and had no interest in academic studies. In this context, I experienced my next encounter with anger: my mother's angry and desperate outbursts in response to my antics. Many parents get angry and scream at their kids. Many parents do it because this is how they were brought up. It becomes a family tradition. Many people defend it passionately (and angrily), saying that it helped them become good citizens. Here is what I observed. As a child I accepted without questioning that anger was the only **logical** response to my problem behavior. When I became a mother, I felt I had no choice but to get angry when my children misbehaved. Since I didn't like being angry and was afraid of the power of my explosions, I tried to suppress my anger as long as I could. And every time my anger erupted, despite all attempts to stay cool and collected, I felt helpless. It felt as if something bigger and more powerful than my regular self was taking me for a ride — and not a joyful one. Hot, unfair, and hurtful words would spill from my lips into the minds and hearts of my own children. Today scientists confirm that emotional patterns in our early relationships (with parents, siblings, caregivers, etc.) become ingrained into our neurology as unconscious programs which automatically run every time an invisible button is pushed.

Once you start thinking about emotions in terms of energy, which can be either healing or destructive, they become easier to understand and easier to master.

I AM Angry

One important thing to understand about the concept of anger as energy is when someone says "I'm angry" we should take it very literally. The energy of anger takes over their mind and body just like the hand of a puppeteer takes control of a puppet. In a way, the person becomes anger embodied. Their chemistry changes. Their physiology changes. They start perceiving their reality differently. Whatever patterns are attached to their anger will unfold, just as surely as a computer program runs when you press "Start." This means that whatever you do when you are angry, you will continue doing until you commit to changing the pattern. Whatever other people do when they are angry, they will keep doing until they commit to changing the pattern.

If a person gets physically violent when they are angry, they will get violent whenever they are overtaken by anger - no matter how remorseful they might feel afterward. If a person's pattern is to get verbally abusive and say cruel and damaging words when they are angry, they will be cruel and abusive when overtaken by anger. It doesn't matter how much regret they feel later or how profusely they apologize. It's a pattern. It runs whenever it is triggered.

This is something I especially want to communicate to all women. People will justify their anger and try to blame **you.** If you yourself are prone to anger, even you will try to justify your anger by blaming others. Some individuals have elevated this skill to the level of gaslighting. "You made me angry. You just had to use a tone of voice that makes me mad." "No, I didn't say that. You are overreacting." "You did it on purpose. You know that makes me mad." "It is all your fault."

Having anger doesn't make you a bad person. It just means you are more likely to say words and take actions which a calmer version of you would not. It means you need to take a good and honest look at what you **actually** do when you are angry, without trying to justify it. The nature of energy is such that it is easier to manage when it is less intense. The bigger the storm, the harder it is to weather it — and the easier it is to get shipwrecked.

Before I became a student of the Tao, I did my best to keep my anger bottled up. That was the only way I knew how to control it. I didn't know that by suppressing and disowning it I made it even more destructive and dangerous. I also didn't realize it was impossible to block only one feeling. The price we pay for the illusion of self-control is the loss of our soul fire.

When I started studying with Master Chia and learned that all emotions are energy that can be mastered, I folded my hands in gratitude.

Is it possible? Can I learn to feel my feelings, be alive in my body, and finally face my most powerful emotions — without letting them cause pain and destruction? I knew I would probably have to undertake many years of meditative practice before I mastered my mind. But I needed it sooner. I couldn't wait that long! Then I remembered I was a hypnotherapist. So I started exploring my most powerful emotions through hypnosis while making sure I did my Taoist emotional alchemy practices.

My Past Life Experience

My hypnotic journey through anger started with a session in a hotel room, where a fellow hypnotherapist ripped the anger energy from my body. I kid you not; it was a bizarre experience.

She asked my permission to touch my abdomen, and then proceeded with grabbing something invisible and forcefully pulling it out with a loud yell, "Go away — you do not belong here!"

Weird as it was, I suddenly, felt lighter and freer. Something dark and heavy was gone from my energy field forever.

After this episode, I had enough control to continue working with this energy on my own. One technique I used was Past Life Regression. It is a hypnotherapy technique I often use with my clients during which a troublesome feeling is traced back to a previous life. It doesn't matter whether it is real time travel, or just a story the mind tells itself. What results from such journeying is often profound and transformative. My meditation practice helped me become really good at self-hypnosis; past life regression included.

I asked my deep mind, "Please, help me understand my anger." And I started going deeper and deeper into my inner journey.

...I was a circus performer. She loved the thrill of dangerous aerial tricks. She was flying and somersaulting, spinning and leaping, basking in the limelight, and reveling in admiration and thunderous applause.

...I see her in her dressing room. She is terribly upset and agitated. She just learned that her lover, with whom she imagined a lifetime of happiness together, left her for another female performer. She is crying at first. Then she flies into red-hot raving rage, screaming and thrashing the furniture in her room...

...Here she is. Quiet and composed, ready to step into the arena and perform the act she knew so well and had performed thousands of times before. Only this time her composure is for the show only, and on the inside she is still shaking with rage and hurt. She leaps. She loses her balance. She falls. There is stunned silence in the audience. Then someone screams. She doesn't move...

As I was awakening from my trance, tears running down my face, I heard the voice of my inner knowing speaking. She said: "When you try to suppress your emotions, they still affect your body. So learn how to take ownership of your energy. When people or circumstances upset or hurt you, the best response is to start nourishing yourself with good energy. Then you become your own healer and your own solace."

I started pouring love and smiling energy into the early memory of my encounter with the angry girl at the boarding school. At first, it seemed nothing changed. Then one day I suddenly felt as if bright healing golden light erupted and enveloped both me and that little angry girl. Only instead of our physical forms, I saw two energies engaged and entangled together. And in that moment, I could feel, see, and experience the truth of the situation. It was never about me. I just happened to trigger her pain and her rage. Her anger and my fear clicked together like two pieces of a puzzle – two energy patterns interlocked into a dance.

The Tao teaches you to deal with your own emotions while they are still small rather than letting them grow so big they start controlling you. Every time I felt angry I started reminding myself that it is my decision to be my own healer and my own solace. I learned to pour love and compassion into my anger to get to the energy essence of the interaction, and see what was real and true.

Eventually, I became really good at recognizing the first signs of anger in myself and others. I became very good at simply melting my own anger with love, and not taking other people's anger personally. I also learned to hold better boundaries with angry people and not let them dump their toxic energy on me. As a little girl, I had no choice. As a grown woman with good boundaries and energy mastery tools, I have much more freedom and power in handling conflicts. I've learned to notice when I start getting angry with my children, and step away from the interaction to release the energy and return to rhyme and reason. I've discovered that humor helps a lot, and seeing the funny side of a situation often allows me to find a better, kinder, and more creative solution to parental woes.

When you start smiling into your anger and healing it with true unconditional love, you melt away the pain, and you are rewarded with new wisdom and new strength. This is the path to deeper healing.

Persistent anger is like a cancer which can spread to all aspects of a relationship until it destroys intimacy and trust. I had to stop justifying and accepting anger directed toward me in order to stop justifying and accepting my own anger toward others. Once I realized how ridiculous it was to blame others for my own lack of emotional energy mastery, I could accept full responsibility for my energy and emotions. The next step was to learn how to deal with this energy.

Clearing Toxic Anger from Your Body

How do you know if you are holding anger inside your body? It might manifest as tension in your chest and jaw areas. It also might make itself known through feelings of irritation, frustration, disappointment, and displeasure. Your heart might feel heavy and tight. You might also be disconnected from joy, pleasure, and fun. Chronic anger creates a certain neurochemistry incompatible with love, joy, and pleasure. But guess what? If you commit to intentionally creating a neurochemistry of love, joy, pleasure, and (above all) compassion and kindness, you will create a neurochemistry and physiology incompatible with chronic anger.

In Taoist traditions, anger is a negative emotion of the liver, while rage and hatred are negative emotions of the heart. The liver is connected to the wood element (green color) while the heart is connected to the fire element (red color). The wood energy of anger will feed the fire energy of hatred and rage. This might lead to overheating the heart, which will spill negative energy into the small intestine affecting digestion, and to the solar plexus, affecting the spleen, pancreas, and stomach, which hold the negative energy of self-doubt and mistrust. When it spreads to the lungs, it might activate the negative energy of sadness and grief. If it spreads to the kidneys, it might trigger fear, which in turn might grow more anger in the liver, and more rage and hatred in the heart.

To break this negative cycle, start with releasing the anger from your liver and heart. Then proceed with replenishing the positive energy in these organs through a loving smile and the visualization of vibrant colors and nature elements.

Taoists discovered that all organs are connected to certain sounds. The liver is connected to the "shh" sound (think of putting your index finger to your lips and asking people to be quiet); while the heart is connected to the "haw" sound (round your lips, open your throat and exhale without vocalization).

Let's Do This!

1. Sit comfortably with your feet on the floor. Imagine your feet growing deep roots, connecting you to the earth. Take a few deep cleansing breaths. Smile and bring your attention to the liver. Smile into your liver and imagine it glowing in green light.

2. Look deeply into your liver. Move your eyes left and right as you look into the liver. Notice any dark, murky, cloudy, or toxic energy. Smile into this energy. Smile into your anger.

3. Inhale and slowly exhale while creating the "shh" sound. Imagine releasing dark, cloudy, toxic energy into the ground. Rock your spine to help move energy. Repeat a few times until you feel a release. Taoist Masters advised doing this in nature, preferably near a stream or a river. If you are in nature, you can stand barefoot on the ground (weather permitting) and imagine releasing your negative energy into a flowing river.

4. Smile into your liver, and imagine replenishing it with green energy from trees and green mountains. Smile, breathe, and grow the positive energy of kindness, which will help to reignite the fire of unconditional love in the heart.

5. Smile into your heart, and imagine the warm glow of red light. Look left and right into your heart, and notice if there is any negative energy of rage, hatred, resentment, cruelty, or judgement.

6. Inhale and exhale with a "haw" sound, releasing all the negative energy into the ground.

7. Smile into your heart and replenish the energy of unconditional love by imagining sunshine, warm loving fire, and the color red.

8. Repeat the process nine times. Release any remaining negative energy into the ground each time.

9. Finish the meditation with the Inner Smile Five-Element Creating Cycle described in the previous chapter. Smile all over yourself and send love to those you love and the planet Earth.

Unconditional love in your heart will feed trust and confidence in your spleen, pancreas, and stomach, which will help bring back courage in your lungs, and tranquility in your kidneys. Then you can nourish your liver with calmness and tranquility, growing more kindness which helps feed the fire of love. As you grow more unconditional love, you can use it to heal your wounds and soothe your sorrows. You will become your own healer and your own solace.

Chapter 7

Forever Love: Releasing Toxic Grief

In 2013, I was attending my first NLP (Neuro-Linguistic Programming) seminar in Orlando. On stage was the legendary Dr. Richard Bandler, a co-creator of NLP. I was feeling exited, elated, and a bit intimidated by all the amazing trainers, coaches, and therapists attending this event with me. Dr. Bandler said, "Think of a feeling of pure unconditional love. Now think of a person you love unconditionally, or who loves you unconditionally…" He paused and looked at us. I started frantically searching. Of course I had people in my life whom I thought I loved, and who I thought loved me. But I struggled imagining a feeling of pure unconditional love. What does it feel like? What does it mean to love somebody unconditionally?

"If you cannot think of any human, think of your dog…" said Dr. Bandler, looking directly at me.

Yes! This was easy. I had a dog, and I knew how it feels to be loved by a dog.

On Friday, August 25th, 2021, my beloved dog Jackie passed away at the age of 15 years and eight months. He didn't make it to 16.

Where there is a big love, there is a risk of experiencing grief. Grief is important. Grief is a tribute we pay to our loved ones when they leave us. There is no way around it. We have to go through it. But grief is not love.

The Tao teaches that grief and love are very different energies. They feel differently in the body. They affect the body differently. Grief is one of the lowest energy states. Love is one of the highest energy states. In grief the body's energy is so low that even the smallest task takes forever. Every movement becomes a strain, an enormous energy expense.

Love in its pure form is healing and life-giving. Grief feels like death.

I knew I loved and missed my dog. I also knew that I owed it to my dog, my family, and myself to find my way through grief back to love. I wanted to learn how to be grateful for my dog, and how to love his life journey even when it was over. Yet I couldn't shake the feeling that my life had lost its purpose and vibrancy, as if nothing mattered anymore. Grief is something for which you cannot prepare yourself. It hits you like a train and leaves you a wreck no matter what you know, or how many self-development seminars you've attended. Grief can age you faster than any unhealthy habit ever will. Grief can trigger a return to unhealthy habits. Grief can fester for years. Sometimes grief can be fatal.

Grief is necessary. But grief is not love. It is different energy, different chemistry, different way of being.

On my journey from grief to love, I reflected in my deep meditations on the lessons of unconditional love. Here is what I learned about unconditional love from my dog.

1. Unconditional love never compares.

A dog loves their human. Period. They do not care if another human is taller, stronger, smarter, has a bigger yard, or more education. I loved my dog. Period. I knew that there were other American Eskimo dogs who were better trained, better behaved, more purebred, etc. And it never crossed my mind to look at another dog and think, "Oh, I wish that was my dog."

2. Unconditional love accepts your mess.

So many times I would come home a total hot mess: sad, exhausted, crushed, depressed, and melting into a pool of tears. I would put my arms around my dog and just breathe or cry or sob - whatever was needed. He was there. Just radiating love. Through the years I cried many rivers of tears into the soft fur of my dog. He never complained. This feeling that there was somebody with whom I didn't need any mask, and could just fall apart before I pulled myself together, was precious. And it was so dearly missed.

3. Unconditional love is healing.

Long before I learned energy healing, when my dog was sick I would hold him, focus on my desire to heal him, and project that wish into his furry body. It felt like pouring light into his body. When I was sick, my dog would come closer and put his head on my lap, or lean against me, or snuggle near. And I could feel something flowing from this warm, furry body. Dogs are natural healers because they know how to direct love energy. They do not block or ration it. They just pour.

I decided to become my own dog, and learn to love myself the way my dog loved me. I started with wrapping my grief in love. Then I committed to practicing pouring love into myself even when I was in my least lovable state. Ever since then, I am my own dog. When I fail, when I mess up, when I fall apart, when I feel like a failure, my first action is to put my arms around myself and wrap myself in love.

I teach all my clients how to do The Inner Smile, and pour unconditional love into every organ. Once a person learns to do it with full acceptance, it creates miracles of healing. As I learn to love myself unconditionally and teach my clients how to do it, I learn how to direct and focus the energy of pure unconditional love at the areas of my body and mind which need healing.

As I grieved, I kept directing pure unconditional love toward my departed dog, his loving memories, and myself.

The lessons of pure unconditional love are the best lessons I learned from my dog. True healing starts when we let go of judgement, labeling, and false positivity, and open the secret gate to let the flow of pure unconditional love into our heart. Dogs already know how to do it. They are our teachers and guides in this physical realm. If you've ever loved a dog, you know they love without measure. Their love is not reserved. Their love is not careful. They give you all their heart. They radiate love. They pour it out. They do not ask, "What if I get hurt?" They just love. They do not withhold love. If you are upset with them, they just love you back. If you are angry with them, they love you back. If you abandon them, they will love you until their last breath.

The more I learn to love like a dog, the more I realize we love dogs because they remind us of our true nature. Our true nature is love. Love is our soul essence. To return to this nature, we must be willing to be vulnerable. We must be willing to love in the now without worrying whether we love too much. True love takes no effort. True love knows no fear. True love transcends time and space. For true love, the time is always now. And it does not end with death. It keeps flowing.

Taoist Way to Forever Love

When you and another living being — whether it is a human or a beloved pet — create a bond of unconditional love, you open a channel of energy exchange between your energy bodies. When your loved one departs you might feel you have a gushing wound, because there is all this energy which has nowhere to flow. Heart wounds are wounds. They might feel like a flesh wound, with life force gushing through it, and leaving your body. The love which you can no longer give might create pain and swelling on the inside. Crying, screaming, and expressing your grief helps release this energy. In many cultures, there is a tradition of loud wailing at the funeral.

It is your personal choice how long to grieve and how to grieve. However, if you want to stay strong, vibrant, beautiful, and carry loving memories in your heart for many years — and if you want to feel connected to your loved ones beyond death — you might choose to return to love.

It won't be immediate. You will have to travel through grief. But if you make a choice to travel toward love, Taoist wisdom can help you get there.

1. Create a healing space.

The first step is to create a space for processing grief. This feeling of "nothing matters anymore" serves a very important function of protection. Grief, like a steel sword, cuts all the cords which usually attach you to the world of living. Grief is dying while being alive. So the Tao advises to take it seriously, and let go of any tasks and activities you can postpone or delegate. In many countries, there is a custom where friends and relatives bring food and take over the household chores while the person or family is grieving.

In American culture there is a tendency to keep busy and try to stay positive, concealing the true enormity of grief. So it is easy to succumb to temptations to find a way to medicate pain with sedatives, alcohol, or food. Unfortunately, when unprocessed, grief can become a festering wound which keeps oozing life force. Take your healing seriously, and start with creating a healing space. Surround yourself with non-intrusive support. Get quiet. Sit with your grief.

2. Make a choice to move to love

Next, it is important to realize that your body needs help, and that staying in grief forever has nothing to do with love. Make a choice to move toward healing.

When you make this choice, you can assess your energy. Whether you are dealing with a recent loss or you have been in grief for a long time, become aware of how it feels in your body. Most likely you are leaking energy. You might leak energy from connections which, in the past, were designed for pouring love and care into somebody you love. It could be the opposite. You might experience pressure and pain from energy you hold inside. Any emotion you used to receive and give in this relationship can become an energy leak, creating a hollow empty feeling; or swelling, pressure, and pain. You will have to go from feeling to feeling, from energy to energy, and either seal the connection, or redirect it to yourself.

3. From grief to love with courage and the lung sound

In the Taoist traditions, the lungs are the organs which hold the negative energy of sadness, depression, and grief. The positive energy of the lungs is courage. Taoist sages discovered that certain sounds and movements can help release emotional energy from internal organs. For the lungs, the healing sound is "sss" (produced without vocalization).

Let's Do This!

1. Sit on the edge of a chair with your feet flat on the ground. Make sure your spine is straight and your feet have a good connection to the earth. Imagine deep roots growing down from your feet to the earth.

2. Bring your attention to your lungs. Look into your lungs. Smile into your lungs. See your lungs filled with beautiful white light. With your eyes, heart, and smile, direct smiling sunshine into your grief. Wrap it with love.

3. Hold your hands next to your lungs, palms facing your chest. Using your inner eyes, look left and right into your lungs. Think of all the feelings which impede breathing, or deflate you. Imagine gathering them as gray, cloudy, foggy colors.

4. Exhale with a long "sss" sound, imagining a cloud of gray and foggy energy leaving your lungs. Guide the grief energy down to the ground with your eyes and mind.

5. Place your hands on your knees and imagine grief energy as gray, foggy, cloudy energy flowing down through your arms, fingers, knees, and legs, into your feet to be absorbed into the ground forever.

6. Hold your hands next to your forehead. Move your eyes left and right while looking into your brain. Imagine gathering all the thoughts, beliefs, and perceptions connected to the energy of grief. With a long exhale and the "sss" sound, guide the cloudy and foggy energy down to the ground.

7. Place your hands on your knees and let the gray, foggy, cloudy energy flow down into the earth.

8. Hold your palms next to your chest and smile sunshine, white light, courage, and love into your lungs. Feel good in your lungs.

9. Smile into your heart and send love, joy, and happiness from your heart to your lungs. Imagine connecting with love. Radiate and shine love from your heart, sending love to those you love.

Traveling from loss to love is not easy. There are no shortcuts. Practice diligently. Set your intentions to returning to love. And go day by day, step by step, toward vibrancy, love, and life. Many women discover that when they return to love, they start feeling deeply connected to theirw departed loved one. Once the channels are cleared, connection can be restored. Realizing that love can continue thriving beyond death is a transformative and deeply moving experience.

Chapter 8

Taoist Sexual Alchemy Qigong:
Solo Practice

A lady was talking to a psychoanalyst. "Doctor, I had a dream about you. You were offering me a long cigar. What do you think it meant?"
"You know, my dear, sometimes a cigar is just a cigar."

Sometimes you can accept a cigar is just a cigar. And sometimes you can accept your sexual organs are just organs.

I was looking for a good article on female anatomy and opened the website of a medical clinic. It read: "Clitoris: The two labia minora meet at the clitoris, a small, sensitive protrusion that is comparable to the penis in males. The clitoris is covered by a fold of skin, called the prepuce, which is similar to the foreskin at the end of the penis. Like the penis, the clitoris is very sensitive to stimulation and can become erect."

This is what I learned while studying medical biophysics at the Russian State Medical University. The clitoris is small. It's like the penis, only small.

In fact the clitoris is much bigger than women and men imagine. It does start its development looking very similar to the penis. Then the penis starts growing outwardly; the clitoris grows inward. A small pea-size protrusion is what remains on the surface, and even this part is covered by a fleshy hood.

It is astonishing that even though (I am sure) many generations of male scientists and doctors have had hands-on experience with the female clitoris, until very recently the clitoris was considered a rudimentary and insignificant organ. Oh, how wrong they were!

Here is an updated anatomy of the clitoris, in a nutshell.

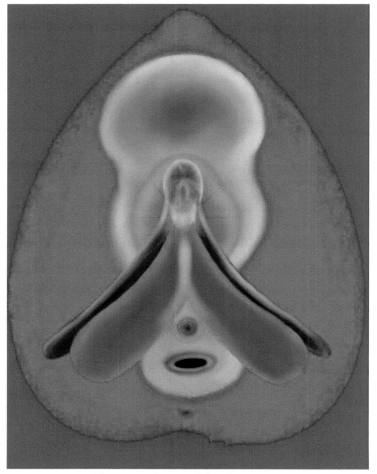

The magnificence of female anatomy

The external part might be small, but it contains more than 8,000 nerve endings. It is similar to the penis because it contains erectile tissue, corpus cavernosa. Below the surface there are magnificent "legs" called crura, as well as vestibular or clitoral bulbs. As research now indicates, the clitoral tissue extends into the vagina's anterior wall. It consists of spongy cavernous tissue, filled with blood and smooth muscle tissue. It is densely innervated (supplied with nerves) throughout the tissue.

In the past, the length of the clitoris has been measured as ranging between 3 and 10 millimeters. With the crura, the clitoris measures from 5 to 7 centimeters (2.0–2.8 inches) in length, while the clitoral body and crura together can be 10 centimeters (3.9 inches) or more in length.

Let's now look at the vaginal canal. In medical terminology, the vagina refers specifically to the canal without any external parts. What is important to know is it's an elastic tube with connective and muscle tissue. It has to be lubricated and aroused to open and allow the penis in without damaging the walls. It has a complex system of ligaments which supports it. The ligaments have to be flexible, moist, and elastic to allow vigorous movements of the erect penis without causing discomfort and damage. The older we are, the more important it is to use our female parts correctly — and take very good care of them.

Now let's talk about truth. Do you believe there are things that are undeniably true?

One truth is we all need to breathe. If you have any doubt, try holding your breath. (The author is not responsible for readers going too far with this experiment.)

We need water. We need food. These are undeniable truths. The force of gravity pulls us down. Even if we don't believe in gravity, it still works.

The reason we need to breathe and eat food is because our bodies are made from trillions of little cells. Some scientists estimate there are 37.2 trillion cells in our body. They are very small so you can't see them, but they are real. They all need oxygen and nutrients. They need to get rid of toxins. They need water to stay moist. And they need protection against damage.

Your sexual organs are organs.

No matter what you believe, how you feel, or what your cultural conditioning is regarding your organs, they are organs. They need the same things as any other organ.

Once you understand this, you will understand the practices I will share with you in this book.
Everything I say about your organs can be applied to your sexual organs and your skin as well.

Don't Look! I'm Naked!

So many women cannot stand looking at their own naked body. It's no surprise there are many women who won't allow their man to turn on the lights when they make love, or look at their sexual organs. Making love is one thing. Looking is another.

If feeling beautiful can transform the way you hold your body, so can feeling ugly. When a woman feels ugly, invisible, and unlovable, her whole being collapses. The slumped shoulders and depressed posture of a woman lacking personal confidence affects her breathing and circulation. The open shoulders and fluid movements of a woman who is confident help fill her lungs with oxygen, and stimulates blood flow.

Your personal confidence determines how others perceive you. It also determines how your body feels, and how your muscles and ligaments are aligned. This, in turn, can affect the functions of your internal organs. Many women feel deeply dissatisfied with the way their body looks. But you cannot heal your body with shame and guilt. You can only heal with love.

My journey to sexual energy activation started long before I met Master Chia.

It began when I read a little book that had been translated from English into Russian. Later when I tried to find this book in America I couldn't; I suppose the title and author's name were hopelessly lost in translation. In this book the authors discussed their work as psychotherapists, helping men and women restore their sexual relationships. According to this book, the one thing that consistently upset men in their intimate relationships was a woman's shyness around her body. The most common sentiment was, "I love her. I want to see her body. It turns me on. But she doesn't let me see her. It kills my desire." The authors made a surprising claim. "Any woman, regardless of age, appearance, and body shape, can seduce and ignite a man with her naked body when she loves her body and is proud to show it." They believed a woman who knows how to pleasure herself and is comfortable doing it, who is proud of her body and comfortable showing it, and who can be fully present and engaged when making love will never lose her man. They even warned about using these special powers with caution so as not to infatuate the wrong man. "Warning! You might not be able to get rid of that man."

I vowed to learn how to feel comfortable, confident, and sexy in my body. I vowed to start loving my naked body, and find pride and admiration in my body so I could radiate this sense of confidence outwardly. But there was one problem. I could only feel good about my body and comfortable showing it if I were 100% percent sure my man loved me. I was clingy and insecure. I was very good at pushing my men away with my constant doubt, jealousy, and questioning. "Do you really love me? I mean really? Truly? What about now?"

The Flower of Life

It wasn't until I started studying with Master Chia I realized the full importance of loving my own body regardless of whether I was with a man or alone; naked or fully clothed. Loving myself. Unconditionally. Magical!

What if instead of finding fault, you learn how to appreciate your body's magic — and how to use its many powers? And what if you started seeing in your female organs the symbol of your beauty and power: a magnificent flower of life?

Sacred Feminine Vitality Practices

Ancient Taoists believed sacred sexual vitality practices did not necessarily require a partner. It was up to a woman to either train her man, or help her sexual organs feel gentle pleasure by engaging in solo practices.

Think of your body as a vessel for your energy. Imagine all your blood vessels, lymph vessels, bronchioles, and nerves as colorful pipes through which you can move your energy. Imagine your muscles as little pumps moving energy. And imagine your fascia layers as bubble wrap supporting your organs, and protecting them from sagging down.

When people get older their muscles can start weakening, and their fascia can get loose and saggy. This is especially relevant to women after 50 when they begin to enter menopause. Many women do not know the female sexual hormone, estrogen, is a protective umbrella nature holds over their bodies. Men experience their own version of menopause when their testosterone starts dropping. For them it's a very gradual process. For women it's rather drastic. It's as if nature were holding a woman in loving and caring palms, supporting and nourishing her, and then suddenly — those hands are whisked away.

If women do nothing, a merciless course of events unfolds. Since estrogen is involved in the synthesis of collagen, everything requiring collagen to function takes a hit. This includes a woman's skin and reproductive organs. Skin becomes noticeably more wrinkled, breasts become increasingly saggy, the pelvic floor weakens, and the vaginal walls become thinner, more fragile and less elastic. Taoists discovered there are things a woman can do to slow this process down, and even reverse it to some extent.

Their techniques are based on very simple logic. If we keep bringing energy, blood, oxygen, nutrients, and hormones to our sexual organs, we remove all unnecessary burdens. If we remove the toxic emotional energy stored in our organs and make sure our lymph moves well, we can help our organs stay healthy, vibrant, and strong for a longer period of time.

Your body is a very real and physical dwelling for your mind, soul, and spirit (or whatever you call the subtle energy essence of you). As you know, a good house has physical structures which protect its inhabitants. But who wants to live in a dark and cold house with no food or air? Every house also needs water and fire. And every house is not a tightly sealed container, but a system which allows for energy exchanges with the outside world. Learning to tap into your feminine energy and reclaiming your magic doesn't mean wearing skimpy and revealing outfits (unless you want to). Or dancing naked in your backyard (unless you want to). It simply means being connected to your feminine body with pride and a sense of sovereignty. It means walking in your power. It means making sure your sexual energy flows abundantly through every cell and fiber of your body. It means being vital and alive in your female body.

Life is Movement and Movement is Life

Without movement there is no flow, and without flow there is no life. In the distant past, female animals had a tail. Imagine walking on all fours making gentle and gracious sweeps with your long tail. If you still walked on all fours and had a tail, you would not need this book. Your tail would vibrate your spine and activate your energy flow, and your muscles would move blood through your pelvic area. Unfortunately, women lost their tails and learned to walk upright, creating a very difficult life for their female organs. This is why you need to really move at least once a day. You must move not only those muscles you typically use to walk, run, drive your car, and perform your work, but also the muscles mostly neglected and inactive during your day.

Stand up and allow yourself a wild little dance. Move your butt, move your thighs, move your calves, stand on your toes, rotate your hips. Dance with a broom or on your own. Shake your booty, touch your toes, raise your arms, and reach for the sky. Breathe deeply to feel alive and to get your energy moving. Moving your entire body is an essential practice. But it's not enough to activate your sexual energy.

Imagine a very dry sponge. If you pour water directly on it, the water will just run over it without getting in. To rehydrate that dry sponge you need to gently dip it into water and squeeze. And release. And squeeze. And release. Your female organs have a lot of spongy tissue, which needs to be hydrated, detoxed, and oxygenated. Your ligaments need good hydration to stay elastic and flexible. Taoist sexual vitality practices include squeezing and releasing muscles, which help move blood and fluids through the tissues.

Do it right now. Gently pull up your pelvic floor and notice the feeling of a squeeze. Now release. Squeeze again. Release. Notice how you start feeling more alive and flowing.

When you squeeze and release you also take care of your lymphatic system.

Inside every tissue there is a system of channels: the lymphatic vessels. These are lined with a single layer of flattened, loosely connected endothelial cells — the same type of cells lining our capillaries. Because lymphatic ducts have such loosely-lined walls they leak fluid into your tissues, and allow the leakage of more concentrated contaminated waste matter into them. Being alive means producing waste. That's a sad and uncomfortable truth. But if we ignore it, we end up spending thousands of dollars on expensive cosmetics and exercise programs while our cells drown in garbage.

Lymph vessels are your sewers. Their job is to clean your tissues. They also replenish tissues with moisture. It is extremely important for your sexual organs to have good lymph flow. Without good flow your cells can drown in waste, and no cleansers or soaps can remove the toxic debris suffocating your cells. Tiny lymphatic vessels flow into larger vessels, until they carry their waste-loaded fluids into the lymph node. Nobody really knows exactly what happens inside the lymph nodes. They are not easy to study. But we know the outflowing lymph is somehow detoxed and regenerated. Lymph vessels are passages for the cells of the immune system, where they patrol the body looking for any foreign matter, aberrant cells, viruses, and bacteria. With age lymphatic vessels decline, which makes waste removal more difficult and less effective. Lymph only can move through your body by the stretching, moving, tensing, and relaxing of the tissues. If you want your sexual organs and skin to enjoy a cleaner and more vibrant inner landscape, you have to make sure your lymph moves through your skin and body.

Your female organs — your breasts and your vagina — have to be detoxed. Lymph has to flow through them to carry out waste. If you want to take good care of your female parts, squeeze and release! Squeezing and releasing gets the job done, and helps move lymph to ensure cleaner and more vibrant living conditions for your cells.

If you can move blood and lymph properly through your body, including your sexual organs, and if you can ensure your cells receive enough oxygen, it'll be a lot easier to keep your sexual energy vibrant and your passion flowing.

If you can think of your sexual organs as organs, you are halfway to enlightenment and sexual vitality. The rest will be easier.

Let's Do This!

1. Think of a time when you needed to go to the bathroom to go "number two" and had to wait. Use the same muscles to gently squeeze your anus. Release. And squeeze and release. Do it nine times.

2. Now think of a time you wanted to pee. Gently squeeze the same muscles you use to hold your pee in. Squeeze and release.

3. Now bring your attention to your perineum, the space between your anus and sexual organ. Pull it up and release.

4. Finally, gently squeeze all three areas and release. Do it nine times. Being gentle is the key. Use your mind and your smile to draw energy to your sexual organs.

If you forget everything else from this book, remember this one thing - squeeze and release gently!

How to Use Yoni Eggs

Yoni eggs are beautifully carved and well-polished stone eggs. Just holding them in your hands is delightful and healing. They feel very different from Kegel balls, which are used for Kegel pelvic floor exercises. They do not feel medical. They feel like part of a sacred ritual — and that is exactly what they are for. Yoni eggs come in small, medium, and large sizes. Start with the medium one to see how it feels. The stone can be any stone, but many women like to choose one which resonates with their energy. Books on gemstone energy can be of help in choosing your egg. Or you can just purchase whichever stone egg appeals to you aesthetically.

When you receive your stone, discard whatever string it comes with. You are going to use dental floss (original unflavored, not mint), and discard it after each use. Take your dental floss and measure out a length approximately from your elbow to the end of your fingers. Fold the floss in two, and thread the folded end through the hole. Now you have a loop of floss on one side, and two loose floss ends on the other side of the hole. Thread the loose ends through the loop and let it tighten. The egg is now secure, and you have enough length to hold onto.

Yoni Eggs come in different colors and can be made from various gemstones.

Let's Do This!

1. Wash your egg thoroughly with soap and hot water. Boil it before the first use. (Quartz eggs are the exception; they should not be boiled.) Be sure you wash your egg after each use. Store it in a dry and clean place. Consider putting it under sunlight or moonlight once in a while to clear its energy and recharge it. Definitely use full moon energy to recharge your egg.

2. The first time you use it, insert your egg while lying down on your back. Warm it in your hands before inserting. Put it between your breasts or next to your heart. Smile at your egg and send love energy to it. You can use a lubricant to ensure it slides in easily. Hold the thread and insert the egg, blunt end first.

3. When the egg is in, gently tug at the thread, but do not pull the egg out completely. This gentle pull is to alert your body to something new needing attention. If you do not feel your egg, don't be alarmed. It's not lost. Tug the thread gently to stimulate your feeling awareness.

4. Relax and smile into your yoni. Remember what you did with the pelvic floor? Gently pull your perineum up, and gently squeeze and release your vagina a few times.

5. If your yoni is strong enough, the egg will start moving up and you will feel the thread moving through your fingers. If the egg is not moving, just imagine it moving. Your mind understands first; the body follows.

6. When the egg stops moving up, gently pull the thread so the egg moves close to the entrance. As you pull, exhale a long cleansing breath. Imagine dark, cloudy, and toxic energy leaving your body. Then repeat Steps 4–6. To make the process more powerful, exhale forcefully with your tongue sticking out.

7. When you are ready to complete the practice, gently pull the egg all the way out. Smile into your yoni and think love, joy, happiness, and gratitude. Wash the egg and store it in a clean, dry place.

When you get stronger, you can do this exercise standing up.
It's better to do the Yoni egg practice in the morning. If you do it before going to sleep you might produce too much energy, and find it difficult to fall asleep.

Benefits of the Yoni Egg Practice

1. Yoni eggs have been traditionally used to make the perineum and vaginal muscles stronger and more resilient to aging.

2. Many women confirm that the Yoni egg practice helped them restore fluid secretion.

4. Because of the unique shape of the Yoni egg, it gently moves up and massages the lymphatic vessels in the vaginal walls. There is no better way to detox and stimulate lymphatic flow.

5. Taoist wisdom teaches us that feminine energy is the most powerful energy and can invigorate the entire body.

6. Taoists believe sexual energy is very powerful, but not very intelligent. This is why people often do stupid and risky things when they are overwhelmed by desire. The Yoni egg practice makes your sexual energy move up your spine into your brain, and then back from your brain to your sexual organs. As a result, your sexual energy becomes more intelligent, and your intelligence becomes more powerful.

7. Taoists believed our perineum could be trained to become the spiritual muscle – the "Chi muscle." A well-trained perineum allows women pull earth energy up into the body. Higher spiritual practices in Taoism involve using the Chi muscle to move sexual energy, and transform it into a more purified spiritual energy.

8. Taoists believed that moving sexual energy up with Yoni eggs helps a woman stay radiant and beautiful.

The benefits you will receive, of course, will depend on your age, your physical condition, and the amount of time you practice every day. Start where you are. Commit to your practice. When you do it regularly, you will notice the difference.

Breast Massage

No matter how big or small, floppy or firm, perky or sagging, voluptuous or modest, your breasts need your attention. Just like your vagina, perineum, ovaries, and uterus, your breasts are organs that require the same things as other organs do: good circulation, oxygen, lymph movement, detox, and energy flow.

This means you have to learn how to massage them.

Massage your breasts in gentle circular movements around your mammary gland. Start with an outward movement and massage nine times. Then change direction and massage your breasts in a circular inward movement, nine times again.

Gently cup them in your hands and bounce them up and down just enough to keep the circulation going.

You can use scented or non-scented massage oil, or no oil at all. The key is to be gentle. There should not be any discomfort or pain.

Pelvic Floor Solo Practices For Women

1. Bring your attention to your anus. (Remember the "need to go number two" feeling.) Just as when you need to hold something inside, squeeze your anus. Relax and smile into your anus. This part of your body is very important. According to the Tao, when the anus gets loose we start losing our energy. Squeeze and relax your anus nine times, and keep smiling into it.

2. Now pull your anus up. Do it nine times.

3. Separate your left anus and right anus muscles. Even if you can't, just imagine you can. Think of all the left side organs sitting on your left anus.

Pull the left side up and imagine it lifting the left side organs up. Do the same with the right side of your anus. Lift nine times on each side.

4. Now think of a time you needed to pee. Remember this feeling? Gently squeeze and pull up your vagina. Imagine you can close it the way a flower closes its petals, very gently.

5. Put both your thumbs on your navel. When you do that, your pinkie fingers will land approximately over your ovaries. Breathe into your ovaries.

6. Now imagine your cervix and the mouth of the uterus. As you breathe, imagine gently closing and opening it. Even if you no longer have your uterus, you can imagine the energy space; your sacred womb space. As you breathe and imagine, you will feel your sexual energy moving.

The Microcosmic Orbit

Every cell in your body produces electricity. Billions of cells working together generate enough power for your body to move, think, feel, dream, digest food, regenerate, heal, make love, and go on fun adventures. Your thoughts are structured energy. Your feelings are embodied thoughts. Your mind inhabits your body and animates it. Your mind is powered by energy, and is made of energy. Your life force is a golden reservoir of energy within your physical body, and every organ receives nourishment from it. Your beauty and radiance, your sexual allure, your feminine force, and your physical body are all powered by the same energy.

Taoists of the past didn't know modern anatomy, physics, biochemistry or neurology. Yet they understood electrical energy flowed in a closed circuit. If there is a break in the wiring, the current stops and the whole system goes dark. Fortunately, our body is designed with many safeguards in place. If electricity is blocked in one area, the body knows how to reroute the current. Yet in order to properly nourish the entire body — including organs which are open to the outer environment such as skin, lungs, and sexual organs — it's important to ensure our river of gold flows through every organ, tissue, and cell.

The Taoists noticed some of our organs seem to be capable of generating and storing more energy, and could serve as batteries or reservoirs of energy. Modern science confirms our mitochondria — our cellular generators of electricity — are more abundant in our brain, heart, intestines, and sexual organs. The Taoists envisioned a circuit connecting our main energy centers, ensuring the flow of energy evenly and smoothly throughout the body. They called it the Microcosmic Orbit.

The Microcosmic Orbit consists of two energy channels which can be connected by placing your tongue on the roof of the mouth.

Let's walk through these channels.

The Yang (or Governor) channel starts at the perineum, and goes through the perineum and coccyx, through the sacrum, up your spine, into your neck, all the way to your crown, down to your third eye and mid-eyebrow, into the center of your brain, and to the roof of your mouth.

The Yin (or Functional/Conception) channel goes from the point just below the lower lip, down to your throat, down to your heart center (not your physical heart, but a point located about two inches from the tip of the sternum), down your solar plexus to your navel, and down to your perineum.

As you use your mind, your inner eye, and heart to direct the flow of energy through each channel, energy from major energy centers gets evenly distributed throughout the body so there are no excesses or blockages. As a result your skin develops a radiant beautiful glow; your posture grows more upright and confident; your sexual energy nourishes your brain; and your mind power rejuvenates your sexual organs.

The Microcosmic Orbit starts and ends in the navel. It transforms you into an integrated individual with your mind, body, and spirit flowing together, and elevating your energy vibrations.

The Microcosmic Orbit is a route which encircles your body, going through your spine along your back, and your midline along your front.

There are some major energy points you'll want to acknowledge as you move your mind and your spine through the Microcosmic Orbit.

1. **Navel:** This is the point which used to connect you to your mother through the umbilical cord. Taoists believe you still receive nourishment from the Universe. This is also a point of vulnerability. In the Taoist tradition there is a cauldron behind the navel where we can store and transform energy. Under the navel is the stove: the fire which heats the cauldron, helping alchemical reactions.

2. **Pubic Bone:** This is the sexual energy center, and corresponds to the ovaries and uterus.

3. **Perineum:** In the Taoist tradition this is called The Gate of Life and Death. Taoists believed many people leak energy through this gate. By training the perineum they believed we can prevent energy leaks, and can pull energy from the earth into our body. They called the perineum the Spiritual Muscle.

4. **Sacrum**: This is a triangular flat bone with eight holes to allow the spinal nerves to branch out. Taoists believed it's important to keep the sacrum warm and flexible. This is why they recommend rotating the sacrum.

5. **Lumbar Vertebras 3 and 4:** This point opposite the navel is called the Doors of Life. Taoists believed we can breathe energy into it.

6. **Thoracic Vertebra 11**: This point on the spine opposite the solar plexus is

called the Adrenal Glands Point, and corresponds to the Kidneys' Fire. Kidneys' Fire represents the emergency energy stored in the kidneys.

7. **Cervical Vertebra 7:** This is a protruding bone at the base of your neck, and is a point opposite the throat center.

8. **The Crown:** This is your connection to the Universe. Taoists believed we can extend our crown like an antenna and draw energy from the Universe.

9. **The Third Eye and Mid-Eye Brow:** These are intuitive centers. You can look out of your third eye and connect to the Universal love.

10. **The Throat Center:** This is a soft spot between your collarbones. When it's open you can express yourself clearly, confidently, and freely.

11. **The Heart Center:** This is in the middle of your chest, less than two inches above the end of your sternum. When your heart center is open you can radiate love and connect to people. Hatred and other negative emotions held in the heart can cause the heart center to close. Smiling loving sunshine into your heart helps your heart open, and become soft and flowing. For women, the heart center is connected to their sexual energy. If the heart center is closed, sexual energy might start to dry out.

12. **The Solar Plexus:** This area under your ribcage where your ribs come together is like a small sun. Smiling into this center helps nourish all your other organs. Taoists believed if the organs are filled with negative energy they can start dumping it into solar plexus. Breathing and smiling into the solar plexus helps clear the negative energy, and opens your sunshine.

I recommend starting with each individual energy center. Take a few minutes to smile and breathe light and vibrant colors into one or several of these centers, imagining dark and cloudy energy flowing out into the ground. When you memorize them, you can start connecting them together through the following meditation.

The Microcosmic Orbit Meditation

1. Sit straight on the edge of a chair. Rock your spine gently. Take a few deep breaths and relax. Smile into your spine.

2. Bring your attention to your navel and smile into it. Feel your navel getting warm and flowing. Imagine a ball of energy, or Chi, rotating behind your navel.

3. Touch your pubic bone and breathe into it. Exhale the Chi to your pubic bone. Breathe into your pubic bone.

4. Contract and pull up your perineum. Move the Chi into your perineum.

5. Gently tap your tail bone. Inhale into your perineum, and imagine pulling the Chi up to your tail bone. Exhale, keeping the Chi in your tail bone.

6. Gently tap your sacrum. Inhale into your tailbone, and imagine pulling the Chi up your sacrum. Exhale, keeping the Chi in your sacrum.

7. Inhale and imagine pulling the Chi up the spine all the way to the base of your skull.

8. Gently tap the base of your skull and mentally pull the Chi there. Finally, bring it to your crown.

9. Put your tongue on the roof of your mouth.

10. From your crown exhale in one slow long breath, allowing the energy to flow down through your forehead, mid-eyebrow, sinuses, roof of your mouth, tongue, throat, chest, solar plexus, and into your navel.

11. Keep the Chi moving through the orbit, directing it with your attention and focus.

12. When you are done, collect the Chi in your navel by massaging your belly from the navel outwardly; then from the outer rim of the abdomen inwardly, condensing the Chi at the navel.

The more you flow your mind through the orbit, the more it becomes a part of you, and the more your Chi flows like a river nourishing your body.

Watering Your Garden

"What is the difference between 'like' and 'love?'

When you like a flower, you pick it.

When you love a flower, you water it daily."

I found this wisdom on Facebook — a place where so many people find their daily inspiration nowadays. These little quotes, memes, and bits of wisdom from Rumi, Buddha, and Einstein, whether real or wrongly attributed, are like droplets of water watering our collective soul garden. They feel good.

When you just like yourself, you can still neglect and abuse your body.

When you truly love yourself, you water your garden daily.

Taoists believed that sexual energy in a women's body is like water. Without water, nothing grows. So often, this energy is wasted on joyless sex, entertainment, shopping, and envying what others have.

Taoists believed that sexual energy wants to couple with other energies. This is why it's so easily tricked by advertising. Everything shiny, sparkling, luxurious, flashy, and rich attracts this energy. And of course, everything which subtly hints at sex attracts it as well.

Taoists believed we can learn to use sexual energy to replenish energy in our organs.

Let's Do This!

1. Lie on your back and relax. Warm your hands, and begin to gently massage your breasts inward and outward in circular motions.

2. When your breasts start feeling warm and vibrating, put one hand on your left breast and the other on your spleen. With a loving smile, guide this gentle warm flow into your spleen. Relax and smile.

3. Massage your breasts again and smile into them. Put one hand on your left breast and the other on your lungs. Use your loving smile and your inner eyes to guide the warm flow into your lungs.

4. Repeat this process with your kidneys and liver.

5. Cup your hands over your breasts and imagine beaming and radiating this energy through your skin. Smile the energy all over yourself. Wrap yourself in it like a warm, soft blanket.

6. Put one hand on your heart and the other on your sexual organs. Breathe from your heart into your sexual organs. Breathe from your sexual organs into your heart.

7. Put your thumbs on your navel and cover your belly with your palms. Become aware of your ovaries; they will be located where your pinkie fingers are. Gently breathe your fresh vibrant life force into your ovaries, and exhale dark and cloudy energy.

8. Wiggle your toes and smile all over yourself.

9. Come back refreshed and energized.

You just watered your garden.

When you learn to take time to replenish your body with sexual energy, you will start developing a new and exciting relationship with your own body. Being vital means being alive in your body, flowing with an abundant life force. The ancient Taoists knew vitality needed to be cultivated and maintained.

Women are like earth. Water your flowers daily.

Solo Practices for Men

There are specific exercises for enhancing sexual vitality (which enhances overall vitality) which can be practiced by a man. They include testicular breathing, testicular massage, and pelvic floor exercises, which are similar to what you have learned in this book (minus the yoni egg). The complete practices can be found in Master Chia's book *Chi Kung for Prostate Health and Sexual Vigor*.

Chapter 9

Taoist Secrets of Healing Love

Taoist Master Chia says a man's sexual energy is like wood. It is easy to set on fire, and easy to burn out. A woman's sexual energy is like water. It has to be slowly brought to a boiling point. Men are easily aroused, and might be sexually satisfied before a woman has even started to get warmed up. A woman needs more time for arousal. Master Chia said, "Men, you should never sail your boat in rocky waters."

Female sexual organs are delicate and sensitive organs. They love being touched and caressed. Unfortunately, many men are too rough and quick. They use force, and they forget to be gentle and loving. They forget how good it feels to be slow and sensual.

When a woman is young, this is more of a relationship issue. When a woman gets older, this issue becomes much more serious.

In menopause, when estrogen levels drop, the connective tissues in the vagina can become less elastic. The mucous membranes might become thinner and the muscle layer, weaker.

If a man still comes in with full force and moves too hard and too fast, it can create great discomfort for any woman who has entered the very special and unique season of life after 50. It might even lead to damage and accelerated aging.

This is why it's very important to communicate to your man the importance of being gentle. He needs to take the time to arouse your body and create enough fluid.

Taoists believe when a woman is loved properly, her awakened sexual energy becomes her medicine. It can heal her body, mind, and soul.

Let's explore Taoist lovemaking practices, which ensure a woman gets properly aroused and flowing before a man burns his fire out.

Taoist Lovemaking Practices: Soft Entry and Hard Retreat

Taoists distinguished three forms of sex:

1. Physical sex for healing, connection, and pleasure.

2. Soul sex for loving and deepened connections.

3. Spiritual sex for achieving unity with the Universe, and enlightenment.

To properly arouse a woman, a man has to start with her heart.

To properly love her man, a woman has to respect, love, and cherish his penis.

Men are very sensitive to any disrespect or criticism regarding their penis. This damage might never be repaired.

Women are very sensitive to any disrespect or insult to their heart. This damage might never be repaired.

Many women do not understand how sensitive a man is about his penis, and might make derogative or humorous remarks. This should never happen in a loving relationship.

A man might not realize how protective and vulnerable a woman is in all matters concerning her heart. He might make jokes, or fail to pay attention to her emotions. This should never happen in a loving relationship.

Teach your man to respect your heart. Learn how to respect his penis.

If you were in love with a Taoist man, he would start his foreplay by saying gentle words of love, or touching and kissing you gently. The Tao advises to start with the breasts and gently massage the nipples. It's important to be very gentle. Many men are too rough, and cause a woman's body to tense and close. Master Chia advised men to practice their loving touch on a piece of soft tofu. If a man is too rough, the tofu will break.

The best way to learn how you should be aroused is to arouse yourself. Find a time when you are alone, get naked, and start exploring. How should your nipples be touched to create a pleasant, warm, and alive feeling in your body? The Taoists advise following the "milk lines;" areas on the abdomen where our animal ancestors had mammary glands. Massage them gently to activate blood flow.

Next, a Taoist man would start gently massaging the clitoris. Remember the picture of the clitoris? It's bigger than it seems. When the clitoris is aroused its legs, located on both sides of the vagina, start swelling with blood. This activates the flow from secretory glands (a female prostate gland) which hugs the urethra like a sponge. The juices start flowing. This is called "opening the first gate." A man should never attempt to enter the vagina until it's completely juicy and wet. The rule for a Taoist man is "soft entry and hard retreat." When the vagina is soft and flowing, a man doesn't have to have a fully erect penis. It can just slide in.

A Taoist woman has a choice. She can have her clitoris orgasm, or she can pull the sexual energy up her spine into the Microcosmic Orbit, and start spinning her orgasm through the orbit. She can have an orgasm in her entire body.

A man enters when the juices are flowing. However, the Taoist man doesn't let himself ejaculate. If we imagine that a full orgasm leading to ejaculation is a 10, then a Taoist man exits the vagina when he is at 7 or 8. He can also pull his orgasm up his spine into the Microcosmic Orbit.

A man and woman can even start moving their energies through each other's Microcosmic Orbits, which produces a heavenly feeling of unity: two souls melting into each other.

After the first exit, the Taoist man starts caressing a woman's G-spot. He inserts his finger into her vagina and begins gently exploring. The woman tells him when he has found the spot. He massages it very gently until she reaches orgasm again. This is called "opening the second gate."

Once again, she can either choose to orgasm, or pull up her perineum (this is where the Yoni egg practice really pays off) and send the warm orgasmic flow into her Microcosmic Orbit.

The man repeats his soft entry and hard retreat. He exits at a 7 or 8, and pulls his energy up into his orbit.

Next, according to the Taoist process, the man lies on his back and the women sits on top with his penis inside, gently pulling her pelvic floor up and breathing into her ovaries. In this position the penis is uniquely positioned to stimulate the mouth of the cervix. In this position a woman has the maximum chance to achieve a uterus orgasm. This is called "opening the third gate."

Another option is for the man to pull out again after achieving a 7 or 8 level of arousal. He also can stay inside, but hold still and let the energy circulate through his orbit, moving his energy through her, while she moves her energy through him.

On the off chance the man hasn't reached his orgasm yet, the circle of arousal can start from the very beginning.

Practical Considerations

I know what you're thinking. "Where do I find a Taoist man?" One answer is: You can teach your man if he is open to learning. You can also encourage your man to engage in some elements of this practice, such as ensuring your heart is full of loving energy, and your yoni is flowing. And finally, you can start doing your own solo practice.

Sexual energy is very powerful. Sexual energy is like water. When you get it flowing, it nourishes your body, activates your brain, and ignites your creativity and passion.

When a woman owns her sexual energy, loves her body, and knows how to pleasure and activate her own body, she can more clearly communicate her needs and desires to her man. And he is more likely to pay attention.

Chapter 10

Becoming Stronger: Beautiful Skin and Strong Bones

Imagine you are walking through a beautiful garden. You cannot help but admire the colorful, vibrant flowers blossoming all around you. However, beauty is more than what meets the eye. In order for beautiful and vibrant flowers to blossom, you need to take care of the soil. You have to water your garden. You have to ensure your flowers get enough sunshine. And you need to keep weeding and feeding your garden.

Your beautiful skin is the same.

When you look in the mirror or when you look at other people, skin is what meets the eye. Timeless works of literature and women's magazines acclaim the magical powers of youthful, soft, silky, smooth, delicate, and flawless skin. In order to achieve the impossible perfection of eternal youth, many women are willing to invest money, time, and energy; try one "revolutionary" and "advanced" skin remedy after another; and often subject their skin to invasive and risky procedures.

What is missing, however, is the realization that skin is a living, breathing, and constantly renewing and regenerating organ. It might not be possible to have the same skin you were born with at the age or 50 or 60 and beyond;

however, it is possible to have beautiful, healthy, radiant, and luminous skin at any age. It is possible to have skin which will perfectly express your inner beauty as long as you live.

Thousands of years ago ancient Taoists discovered that our internal organs, including skin, renew and rejuvenate from within. They developed powerful practices for balancing and awakening our body's innate wisdom and healing powers.

Today, modern science has discovered that skin indeed has more potential and deeper reserves for regeneration and renewal than was previously believed. Moreover, science discovered that many signs of aging, which in the past were attributed to the passage of time, are not age-related at all, but signs of damage inflicted by external and internal factors. It's now known that stress and negative emotions affect skin even more than environmental toxins and UV-radiation.

If you want to have beautiful skin, you are lucky. Women who want to remain beautiful, confident, and desirable have more access to deep scientific knowledge and an astonishing variety of tools and practices at their fingertips than ever before.

In America women spend billions of dollars on makeup and skin care products every year, trying to look younger and more beautiful. Just visit any drug store or open a women's magazine and you will be overwhelmed with the alluring names of products promising a youthful glow, smooth and radiant skin, and a flawless complexion.

Your skin is designed by nature to be your "interface" – a point of connection between your inner Universe and the Universe around you. Skin receives energy, senses energy, and radiates your unique light.

Stop for a moment and think about it. Here you are with your thoughts, gifts, talents, mistakes, experiences, and feelings. Out there is a world which looks at you and knows nothing about you, except what you present on the outside. And what is on the outside? Your skin.

Think of how many trillions of years of evolution it took to create this biological marvel: a thin, flexible, soft, warm, and attractive wrapping for your body. It can withstand UV-radiation, dry wind, and freezing cold; protect you from toxins, bacteria, and viruses; and shield you from spiky, scratchy, poisonous, dirty, and irritating influences. It's self-repairing too!

Here is what your skin does for you:

1. **Serves as a living shield.** It is a mechanical barrier protecting you from intruders. It can actively fight viruses and bacteria through the actions of the immune system, its acidic mantle, antimicrobial peptides, and friendly skin bacteria, which it hosts.

2. **Protects you from dehydration**. Without skin your body would dry out very fast. Inside your skin there are layers of complex water-holding structures, which allow you to enjoy a hot day on the beach without turning into a dried frog.

3. **Thermoregulation.** Your skin's fat insulates your body while your blood and sweat glands help cool you off. You can maintain a comfortable body temperature without even thinking about it.

4. **Sensing.** Skin is what touches the world and other living beings. Skin is what is being touched by the world and other living beings. Skin is what experiences the warmth of the sun and the coolness of the breeze. Skin is what itches when we put on a sweater gifted by our grandma. Skin is what crawls when we see an unpleasant person. Skin is what tingles with delight at a lover's touch.

5. **Endocrine regulation**. It makes vitamin D when it's exposed to sunlight, and also produces a host of biologically active compounds, including sex hormones. Skin also is responsive to hormones. It feels stress and other emotions.

6. **Detox.** Your skin is the largest detox facility in your body. Skin releases CO_2 (carbon dioxide) and metabolic toxins through its many pores.

7. **Respiration.** Your skin can absorb oxygen from the air and release CO_2.

8. **Social connections.** For human beings, skin is an essential and inevitable component of our beauty. Skin is impossible to ignore. Skin will tell other people how we feel, how old are we, if we're healthy, how much time we spend outdoors, our origin, our race, perhaps even our gender, and much more.

As you can see, skin is vitally important even without taking its esthetic qualities into account. Such a hard-working organ does not have to be eye candy. However, this large and important organ is also visible to others.

Most of your organs are hidden behind your skin. We can see people's eyes and teeth and a bit of the inside of their mouth, but that's about it. Other internal organs are well hidden. You can have clogged arteries, swollen joints, and a damaged heart and still be able to appear strong, healthy, and successful. But not with skin. Your skin exposes you. It tells a tale. It reveals your secrets. And the older you get, the more revealing your skin becomes.

Imagine if people could see other people's inner organs just as easily as they see their skin! Maybe we would notice their decline earlier and take more decisive actions?

Even though many people are not willing to admit how much they care about their skin's appearance, the numbers speak for themselves. Only in the U.S. do people spend more than $8 billion dollars on skin care products annually.

The reason skin products and procedures are so popular is that nowadays good-looking, youthful, healthy, and smooth skin has become a status symbol. A person who has youthful, healthy, and beautiful skin is often perceived as more successful, wealthy, balanced, and even virtuous compared to a person with an uneven complexion, premature aging, inflamed lesions, and coarse, rough skin. Think about an evil witch with warts on her crooked nose. In the age of Facebook and Instagram it has become even easier to put that extra pressure on yourself and yield to the temptation to compare yourself with glamourous images looking at you from your "Friends" pages.

Your skin tells a tale. Your skin reveals your secrets.

In the past, a good doctor could make an accurate diagnosis of a patient's condition just by looking at their skin. Dilated and inflamed blood vessels; a yellowish, bluish, or greenish tint; a pale complexion, bags under one's eyes, various spots and rashes – all these characteristics were used to diagnose conditions of the internal organs.

Many women cannot imagine their lives without skin products and makeup. Whether it is to conceal wrinkles, make lips fuller and more seductive, create an illusion of bigger and more beautiful eyes, or hide dark undereye circles and other tell-tale signs of despair and exhaustion, skin care products are there to help. As women chase the impossible dream of having eternally young and wrinkle-free skin, they fail to realize that their skin, which they paint, oil, scrub, and inject with gels and toxins, is a living and breathing organ which holds within itself its own magic of healing, renewal, and rejuvenation.

Your skin products can help your skin to regenerate, renew, hydrate, and protect itself. However, they cannot replace the biological systems which are already installed into your body and are best designed to do this job. Your skin is your largest organ, which covers your entire body and is exposed to the outside environment. It protects your organs and defines your inner environment. This large and important organ has to be maintained, fed, oxygenated, hydrated, protected, repaired, and regulated. This is a big job, and it involves every organ and system in your body.

Your skin breathes through your lungs, digests food with your digestive system, protects itself with your immune system, and regulates itself with your nervous and endocrine systems. It shines your light, but does not create the light. This light has to shine from your core being.

Pretty Bones and Why They Matter

Most people never think of their bones as something which can breathe, feed, regenerate, and rejuvenate. However, bones are living tissues and they receive up to 10% of your total blood volume pumped by your heart with every heartbeat. This is a lot.

Bones receive oxygen, nutrients, and chemical growth factors, and just like any other tissue they have to get rid of metabolic waste, carbon dioxide, and acid.

Unlike cartilage, which does not have cells or blood vessels, your bones are alive and can regenerate. They can also grow old, brittle, and dry. Blood flows into the bone through nutrient arteries which enter the bone's inner cavity. Then blood travels through the sinuses of the bone marrow and numerous tiny capillaries which deliver blood, oxygen, nutrients, and regulatory molecules into the cortex, where baby bone cells can feed and grow.

As we grow older the blood supply to our bones decline; bones become drier, with less developed bone marrow and less active baby cells. As the bones' inner environment becomes more suffocating and acidic, the bones activate special cells called osteoclasts, which start dissolving and digesting bones. Your bones become weak and are easily deformed.

This is a simple truth. It is not easy for your heart to push blood through all your bones. When you move regularly, your muscles act as additional hearts, pushing blood in. If you sit all day long your bones suffocate and age faster.

Bone marrow is the cradle for your red blood cells and the cells of the immune system. Like all babies they need nourishment and support. When blood flow to the inner bone declines with age, it negatively affects formation of blood cells and your immunity. The percentage of marrow space occupied by hematopoietic tissue goes from a 40–60% range in young adults to a 20–40% range in older people. The rest of the space is taken up by fat.

Your body never runs out of blood because of declining bone marrow, but it spends more energy manufacturing the same amount of blood cells from less available stem cells. What really suffers is the body's immunity, which declines as we age.

You might think that your bones never change but in fact, they do. However, they do it so slowly that most women do not even notice how their face elongates and their body develops the slumped posture of an old person. No matter what cosmetic product you use, your bones reveal your age.

The truth about bones is that they are more important to your beauty, confidence, and sexuality than most people realize. Your bones support your organs, your skin, and your spirit. There is a saying, "You are as old as your spine." There is a lot of truth in it.

When you are constantly grumpy, sad, and depressed, your muscles pull your bones down. Bones are heavy. They need all support they can get. In the Tao it is believed that heavy and toxic emotional energy can accumulate in the bones. When everything pulls your bones down and nothing lifts them up, your face will eventually elongate. Your chin might get pushed back. Your orbital rim might change and open more space for hollows under your eyes.

When the blood supply to your bones declines due to aging, immobility, and illness, your posture, energy, and confidence decline as well.

Bones do take a long time to change, but once they have changed it is extremely difficult to reverse the changes.

In the Taoist practices, bones are viewed as crystals which can absorb and amplify energy. In more advanced practices, there is a technique where you wrap your energy around your bones to make them stronger. When you recharge your body with energy you use your bones to receive energy.

If you ever feel anxious and unstable, tap your bones and feel their solid reality. This will help you return to a more grounded and present state.

Taoists had many great ideas about bones which help us keep our bones healthy, happy, and young today. Most of them take just a few minutes a day to do, but they have a tremendous effect on bone density, vitality, and their ability to absorb good energy to create youthful radiance.

1. Mindfulness practices: By focusing your mind inside your bones you direct energy and blood flow to the bones. Smile into your bones often.

2. Qigong daily warm ups: rotating joints, stretching, and shaking activates blood flow to the bones.

3. Pressing muscles to the bones condenses energy in the bones. It also helps activate blood flow, and sends signals to bone stem cells to grow and regenerate bones.

4. Laughing out loud while directing the vibrations of laughter into your bones. You can laugh into your sternum, hips, femur bones, sacrum, and arm bones.

5. Taoist practices of Tao Yin (Taoist yoga) and Iron Shirt – a standing meditation which helps develop strong bones and maintain good posture. Refer to Master Chia's books, videos, and classes on these practices.

The simple activities of stretching, shaking, and rotating joints mindfully and with awareness — as well as smiling into your bones and laughing out loud until you feel vibrations in the bones — for just a few minutes each day can support your bone health, vitality, and alignment. It will also have a beneficial effect on your skin's radiance and vitality.

Muscles and Movement

The reason you can move is because you have muscles. Muscles support your bone structures and further define your shape. If you are an athletic and active woman you have well-developed muscles which define your body and, most likely, your self-image as well.

If you are an office worker and couch potato, you might have a difficult relationship with your muscles. You know you have to exercise, but you are just always too busy and too tired.

Regardless of how well developed your muscles are, they are important. As you smile and laugh and cry and make faces, your facial muscles pull your skin and slowly change its qualities. Your facial muscles are responsible for your expression wrinkles – "smile" and "frown" lines.

Some people fight expression wrinkles with Botox and some just let them be. In both cases, whether your muscles are pacified by Botox or whether your face is alive with many wrinkled emotions, your muscles support your body, your skin, and your spirit.

This is a very important concept. In the Taoist tradition, there is no separation between your body, mind, and spirit. Western doctors know this too, but they do not practice it. They prescribe pills and procedures for specific organs or specific problems. When an Eastern doctor meets a patient for the first time, they evaluate the entire person – the whole body, emotions, energies, and spirit.

There is a place for the Western approach. However, when it comes to your skin and your beauty, you have to start seeing, feeling, and hearing your body and your energy as an integrated whole.

Your outer beauty is your inner beauty shining out.

This is the way to ageless beauty.

Take a deep breath. Notice that your chest muscles participate in breathing.

Your diaphragm is a big muscle. If you are constantly stressed and have a lot of anxiety, your diaphragm get tense and your breathing becomes shallow.

Take a deep breath again. Let it out. Take another very long and deep breath. Appreciate your diaphragm and chest muscles.
Can you be beautiful and radiant if your breathing is restricted? It would be very challenging. This is why anxiety and stress are so detrimental to beauty. They affect your breathing.
Did you know that with age, muscles might get depleted as well? This condition is called sarcopenia, and it influences your body shape and posture. It also can further weaken bones.

Many thousands of years ago, ancient Taoists discovered something that science discovered only recently. By moving your body regularly you can not only reverse age-related muscle loss, but also restore your bones. As studies revealed, bone density and regeneration are stimulated by mechanical tension created by muscles. The more you move your body, the stronger your bones. There are studies which investigated muscle and bone density in elderly martial arts practitioners which discovered they had the muscle and bone strength comparable to people who were 40 or more years younger. Studies also show that those who only started becoming physically active in middle age still have much less risk of fractures and bone fragility compared to those who do not exercise.

Moreover, there are studies proving that moving your body and training your muscles can rejuvenate your DNA so it starts producing proteins similar to a younger body.

Muscles can regenerate faster than bones. It still takes time to repair a muscle or build a stronger muscle, but it can be done faster than growing new bone tissue. By increasing your muscle strength, you help your bones stay younger, which helps your posture and facial contours to resist age-related changes.

Can you wiggle your toes? Notice how far they are from your heart? Your heart is a muscle too. And it is a muscle which never stops.

Have you ever wondered how your blood comes back to your heart from your toes?

In the past when humans were running, jumping, bending, turning, and walking long distances, their muscles served as extra hearts. Your calves and your thighs and your buttocks are designed to help your heart pump blood back from your toes. If you sit too long, your blood might become stagnant because your heart muscle has to work extra hard to pump blood through the entire body.

Joints, Fascia, and Ligaments

Most Western exercises work on muscles. You can find muscle-supporting supplements in stores. But what the ancient Taoists discovered is that there is another system which supports your body, your skin, and your spirit. It is your joints, fascia, and ligaments.

Your joints are structures which connect your bones, allowing flexibility and movement. You are not walking stiff like a mannequin. You can sway your hips, you can rotate your hips, you can sashay and bend and turn.

It is very important to realize that joints need to be filled with lubricating liquid. This liquid is replenished, detoxed, and rejuvenated with tissue water which is pushed into joints when they move. Your joints do not have their own hearts. They need to move in order to be soft, fluid, and flexible. If you sit too long and do not move, your joints cannot replenish their liquid. The lubricant becomes toxic, heavy, and sticky.

It is very difficult to be alluring, sexy, and confident when your joints are sticky, creaky, and stiff.

Fascia and ligaments are structures made from connective tissue. Fascia wraps your muscles, underlines the muscles of your face, and supports and suspends your internal organs.

Ligaments are like flexible ropes which further reinforce your muscles.

In the Taoist tradition, fascia is regarded as "bubble wrap" which can be filled with energy. Your skin has a layer of fascia which unites all facial muscles into a "mask."

Taoists discovered that by filling fascia with energy (Chi), it is possible to prevent the age-related sagging of inner organs and facial skin, creating a much more youthful appearance.

Your skin has muscles, and these muscles are wrapped in fascia too. In fact, your skin has a unique "mask" – all muscles which help you express your emotions are connected to a large sheet of fascia. The simplest way to activate this fascia is through smiling and laughing.

Modern science discovered that fascia in the skin needs to be hydrated in order for skin to appear younger. When blood flow in skin declines, fascia starts losing water and Chi, so facial muscles starts sagging and pulling the whole face down.

Both fascia and ligaments need to be moist and flexible. They too are replenished, detoxed, and rejuvenated through movements.

Qigong has a great number of exercises which help to replenish moisture in your fascia, joints, and ligaments.

That old picture of an elderly lady with swollen joints, a stiff and crooked back, and sagging body? Get rid of it now. With just a few minutes of Qigong exercises per day, you will keep your body flexible, seductive, fluid, and strong.

It's Time to Start Loving Your Fat

If you are a woman, you might have a difficult relationship with your fat. If you want to look young and radiant, you might want to reverse that feeling and start appreciating your fluffy padding.

Your muscles are wrapped in fatty tissue. Your internal organs are wrapped in fatty tissue. Your skin has a fatty layer supporting it. You might be not that fond of your fat, but it supports your muscles and skin, and it also defines your body and face.

Did you know that if you carry some extra weight in menopause, you might age slower than thin and athletic ladies? In menopause, estrogen synthesis in your ovaries declines. Your fat comes to the rescue and starts making extra estrogen to help your body cope with a sudden drop in female sexual hormones.

Soft and Squishy Parts

Some parts of your body are soft and squishy. They are your lungs, brain, liver, spleen, pancreas, kidneys, small intestine, and large intestine. They are not moving around in your body. They sit where they are supposed to sit, and each of them has their unique job. You cannot move them voluntarily; they have their own mind.

In the Taoist tradition, it is believed that our organs store emotional energy. Modern science discovered that our consciousness has a physical basis and is generated by our neurology. Many organs are now found to have such complex and exquisite neuronal networks that they are believed to have own "mind." Since every organ is a part of the whole, your organs harbor parts of your consciousness.

Taoists have unique and powerful meditations which are like colorful stories your mind tells your organs without words. They might take time to master at first. However, as you tell the same story again and again using colors and images to communicate with your body, the body eventually starts telling these stories to itself. Your body becomes more intelligent, and its wisdom becomes accessible to you.

Instead of making your body the bane of your existence which you exhaust, punish, and fill with shame and hatred, you will live in a body which is your temple, your castle, your sanctuary, and your delight. Your body will become a vessel for your mind, soul, and spirit – a window you use to interact with the world, and a secure safe haven where you can retreat to rest and rejuvenate.

This is the way to a beautiful ageless body, mind, and spirit.

Let's Do This!

1. Stand with your feet shoulder-width and parallel to each other. Imagine that you decided to sit in a chair, but then changed your mind. In the Tao we call it "sit, but not sit." Your spine is straight. Your tailbone is slightly tucked in, and your pelvis is open and relaxed. Lift up your shoulders and then drop

them. Feel them relax and open. Leave some space under your armpits. Imagine your head is suspended from the ceiling by an invisible thread.

Imagine there are roots growing out of your feet into the ground. Feel your bones and your muscles. The Qigong posture trains your body to be aligned with minimal effort. Your blood vessels and lymph vessels are open and flowing. Your muscles do not have to work hard to support your body. You can relax into your body.

Your knees are above your toes – not twisted or locked. The posture should feel easy and natural.

2. Put your mind into your hips and your spine. Wrap your attention around your waist like a loving belt. Start to slowly rotate your hips keeping your attention on your spine, hip joints, and lower abdomen.

Qigong is different from Western exercises because it involves the mind. You do not listen to news or chat on the phone as you do the exercises. You invest your attention into your body. You invest your mind into your practice. You learn to move your mind with a clear and strong intention and precise focus.

3. Tap your sacrum (the flat bone at the base of your spine). Put your palms on your sacrum and just breathe into it. Your mind is moving your breath. First, you imagine it. Then, it becomes real.

4. Locate your tailbone. Now see if you can rotate your tailbone in small circles. Imagine drawing spirals and a figure 8 with your tailbone. This will open energy flow through your spine and add vitality to your sexual organs.

5. Place your hands on your sacrum and breathe into it again. Feel warm and good in your spine. Your spine is your main energy highway. When your spine has an energy traffic jam, your whole body, including your skin, is blocked.

6. Place one hand on your sacrum and another on the back of your skull. Breathe into your hands. Imagine your skull and your sacrum connected and talking to each other.

7. Touch your sternum and laugh out loud, Feel vibrations in your sternum. Touch your hips and laugh out loud. Feel the vibrations in your hips. Hug yourself and laugh out loud into your arm bones.

8. Take a deep breath. Slowly let it out. Relax and smile.

9. Finish the exercises with massaging your abdomen from your navel in widening circles counterclockwise 36 times. Then reverse the movement and start massaging your abdomen from the biggest circle in spiral motions condensing energy in your navel 24 times. Imagine yourself gathering your energy and then condensing it and storing for future use.

Rotating your hips and your tailbone is a vital exercise if you sit too long and you want to keep your spine and your sexual organs healthy and flowing. Just like a hose which kinks and blocks the water flow, keeping your hip joints in a sitting posture blocks your sacrum and impedes the flow throughout your entire body.

This is the way to inner beauty and outer radiance. Your body functions as a whole. To add vitality and radiance to your skin, you have to start thinking and caring about your bones and muscles.

The more you learn how to align them in a relaxed stance, the more you will become aware of the times when you block the flow and neglect your supporting structures.

Please refer to other books by Master Chia for more Qigong exercises for bone and muscle strength.

Qigong — from Qi (or Chi, which means energy) and Gong (work) — is a system of gentle mindful movements developed by Taoist Masters. They are specifically designed to work with your connective tissues, blood vessels, lymph vessels, breathing muscles, and practically every organ in your body, to restore their vitality and energy flow.

Qigong Posture and Rooting Into the Earth

1. This exercise works best when it's done in a beautiful and natural setting. Stand with your feet shoulder-width apart and parallel to each other. Make sure your feet feel connected to the Earth. In the center of each sole, right behind the bones in the base of your toes, is a soft part the Taoist's call "The Bubble Spring." This is a very important point through which your energy connects to the Earth's energy.

Think of a tree. Think of how tall and beautiful it is. The reason a tree can stand so tall and secure is because of strong roots reaching deeply into the ground. Imagine your energy roots extending into the ground. Breathe into your soles and with every breath, let your roots deepen.

2. Imagine you decided to sit on a chair, but then changed your mind ("sit, but not sit"). Your spine is straight. Your tailbone is slightly tucked in and your pelvis is open and relaxed. Imagine there is a beautiful dragon tail which extends from your tailbone, and grounds you into the earth.

3. Lift up your shoulders and then drop them. Feel them relax and open. Your chest is not puffed out, and it is not sunken in. Relax your chest. Release your chest.

4. Leave some space under your armpits.

5. Imagine your head is suspended from the ceiling by an invisible thread.

This basic Qigong posture trains your body to be aligned with minimal effort. Your blood vessels and lymph vessels are open and flowing. Your muscles don't have to work hard to support your body. You can relax into your body.

Stand like a tree. Be stable like a mountain. Feel connected. Feel your body as a bridge between the Earth and the sky.

6. Bend your knees slightly. Keep them relaxed and positioned right above your toes, not twisted or locked. The posture should feel easy and natural.

7. Become aware of your body. Become aware of your feet. Take a nice slow deep breath starting from your soles. Imagine you are breathing in something from the earth.

8. Tap the crown of your head and imagine it opening up. Look up into your crown and smile into your crown. Breathe into your crown.

9. Feel yourself comfortably immersed in the forces of nature. The earth is below, abundant with Yin power. The sky is above, abundant with Yang power. You are nature, moved by a continuous and playful interaction of Yang and Yin forces. You are a beloved child of the Universe. The same energy — which flows through every tree and blade of grass, which moves the planets and illuminates the sky — is flowing through your body. When you are relaxed and open you feel connected. When you have good Chi in your body, heart, and soul, you are open to flow. You radiate vibrant energy through your skin.

Embracing the Tree – Iron Shirt Qigong Posture

Qigong Warm-Ups

1. Stand in the Qigong posture with your feet shoulder-width apart. Remember to keep your spine straight (sit, but not sit), and your lower abdomen open with your tail bone slightly tucked in. Relax and feel your feet growing roots to ground you into the Earth.

2. Slightly shake your body, feeling the smooth and relaxed movements of your limbs and spine.

3. Gently rotate your head to release your neck. Position your head on your neck as if there were a silk thread suspending your head. Imagine there is no effort holding your head.

4. Smile into your body and wiggle your toes. Connect your toes to the ground.

5. Imagine your dragon tail growing into the ground. Feel grounded in your body.

6. Put your mind into your spine and your hip joints. Gently rotate your hips, feeling the smooth movement of your joints. Visualize a lubricating liquid being produced in your joints.

7. Focus on your sacrum. It's a wide flat bone at the base of your spine. Gently tap it. Hold your palms on your sacrum and breathe into it. Then start rotating your sacrum, focusing on your tailbone.

This is not a big movement. In order to be able to move just your sacrum — the bone which is connected to your tailbone — you have to relax.

If you are not sure if you are moving your sacrum, just imagine it moving. Imagine it being flexible and alive. Shine your smile into your sacrum, like radiant sunshine. Imagine you have a long pencil extending from your perineum, and draw an infinity sign or your own name on the ground below you.

Even just focusing on your sacrum and imagining moving it will send more electricity and more life force into your sexual organs.

Taoists say, "You are as young as your spine." For a woman, having a flexible, vital, and pain-free spine is essential.

The Bamboo Hitter Practice

A bamboo hitter is a bundle of thin and light bamboo rods bound together. (It can be ordered through the Tao Garden in Thailand, and other online Tao practitioner resources.) When you hit yourself with it, it does not cause any pain or damage. It does create a vibration of the tissue, which activates lymph movement.

By hitting your thighs and buttocks you activate lymph and blood flow from your legs to your body — including the organs in your pelvic cavity.

Modern science has discovered applying vibrational force helps remove cells which are damaged or sick. Stem cells can then activate and regenerate the tissue. Bamboo hitters are very safe, and can be used every day without any ill effect. You also can fill a sock with dry beans and slap yourself gently with it. You can also use your own hands. Just a few minutes of gently slapping your body helps to move your lymph and activate blood flow. It encourages regeneration.

Chapter 11

The Hidden Cost of Stress: Inflammation and Aging

There is an arsonist who keeps lighting small fires in the big forest, and there is a fire brigade which does its best to extinguish the fire. One day the fire brigade is exhausted, overwhelmed, and overworked, so the fires blaze bigger and bigger until they grow so big they start destroying acres and acres of the forest.

Fire is inflammation. The arsonist is stress, toxins, and other damaging factors; the fire brigade is your body's protective and regenerative systems. And yes, you are the forest.

As a rule, inflammation increases with aging in many living organisms, not only humans. In a young, healthy body, there are natural ups and downs of inflammation in response to stress, toxins, damage or infection. Such waves of inflammation are harmless and subside on their own. However, with age, it appears that the body becomes very vulnerable to developing a chronic inflammatory state, which is characterized by the increased level of inflammatory mediators in tissues. This chronic inflammatory state is often referred to as "inflamm-aging," and it corelates with the increased risk of obesity, cardiovascular diseases, neurodegeneration, and even cancer. One of the inflammatory mediators is interleukin 6 (IL 6). Studies confirmed that elevated IL 6 is a good predictor of age-related frailty and disability.

The exact reason why the body switches to a chronic inflammatory state are still not quite understood. The studies show that one of the drivers of chronic inflammation is disfunction of mitochondria – energy powerhouses of the cell. As mitochondria age, they start generating less energy and produce more toxic free radicals. Therefore, one simple solution to reduce inflammation is to lessen the burden on mitochondria and make them work less and repair more.

This means we need to start eating much less when we age. Another solution is to have periods of intermittent fasting to allow mitochondria to rest and repair. Certain traditional diets, such as the Mediterranean diet, which is rich in minimally processed vegetables, fruits and olive oil, are associated with less inflammation compared to a typical American diet. Many fruits, berries and vegetables are powerhouses of nature's pharmacy and contain anti-inflammatory compounds, which can help the body deal with inflammation. Other factors which lead to increased inflammation are vitamin D deficiency, changes in the gut microbiome, environmental toxins, and stress. It was shown that toxic pollutants are deposited in fat (adipose tissue) and can stay there for a long time, influencing metabolism through affecting biochemical pathways and gene expression.

Free radicals in some amounts are actually needed in the body. They participate in cellular communication, and are part of healthy immune reactions. However, if the body's antioxidant defense is overwhelmed, free radicals of oxygen start triggering oxidation of cellular membranes, proteins and DNA. Free-radical oxidation of cellular lipid membranes produces an avalanche-like cascade of highly toxic free radicals of lipids, which trigger more oxidation and produce more cellular damage. Inflammation appears to be one of the basic responses to cellular and tissue damage. So at some point, damage and inflammation form a self-sustaining cycle and create a chronic inflammatory state.

It is important to understand that some of the factors which lead to the inflammatory state in older people cannot be completely avoided. This is why it is especially important to address factors which are within our control. We already discussed the impact of chronic stress, which might create a chronic inflammatory state by repeatedly activating the fight or flight response. Lowering your level of stress by learning to relax and release negative emotional energy by smiling into it and guiding it down to the ground can help avoid or reduce age-related increase of stress-induced inflammation. Another way to control inflammation is through paying attention to your digestion, gut microbiome and food choices.

In order for your body to make energy and stay alive, you have to breathe and you have to eat. Your lungs and your digestive tract are internal organs, but they are connected to the outside world and allow external matter (air or food) in. Just like breathing polluted air can cause inflammation in the lungs, eating certain foods which contain chemicals foreign to our metabolism can cause inflammation in the gut.

Our large intestine is home to many microorganisms. It is estimated that the total count of all bacterial cells in our gut is somewhere around 10^{13} and 10^{14} (10 trillion to 100 trillion). Incidentally, this is about as many microorganisms as cells in our body (estimated 3×10^{14}). It is established that the gut microbiome is very individual and remains stable through our life time. However, it can be altered by dietary and lifestyle factors. Today we know that the gut microbiome has a way to communicate with our body, and specifically with our brain through a system of chemical messengers produced by microorganisms. Stress can affect the gut microbiome, which in turn might affect our emotional and physiological response to stress. Imbalance in the gut microbiome is linked to such conditions as inflammatory bowel disease, obesity, diabetes, cardiovascular diseases, and neurodegenerative diseases. Sometimes the gut microbiome becomes so altered that it triggers an immune response from the body, which leads to more inflammation and more digestion problems.

Taoist Way to a Healthy Gut

Taoist masters paid great attention to nutrition and digestive health. They developed practices, which are now making more sense from a scientific perspective. First we'll review these practices. Then we'll discuss how you can make it easier for yourself to select food that is maximally beneficial for you — and do it without struggle or stress.

Taoist masters believed that food is a gift that has to be appreciated. They advised us to eat mindfully and avoid unnecessary conversations or any other activities which can take your mind away from eating. They considered it essential to create a sacred space for meals and prepare themselves spiritually for receiving food. Food can be a meditation. We now know digestion is a complicated process, much like a production line in a factory. Each step in the digestion conveyer line prepares the content for the next step of digestion.

The first step begins before food even enters your system. As you look at your meal, smell it and prepare yourself for eating. Your mouth starts producing saliva while your stomach starts producing gastric juices. When you slow down and allow time for looking at your food, smelling your food, and chewing slowly and mindfully, you help the digestive tract prepare for digestion.

The second step is chewing, which breaks food down to smaller bits and mixes them with saliva, which moistens food to help it pass through the esophagus. Saliva also contains the enzyme amylase, which breaks down complex carbohydrates such as starch. Since the stomach doesn't have teeth and doesn't digest starches, if you do not chew well the digestive process in the stomach might be impeded.

The next step is digestion in the stomach. The stomach is a muscular elastic bag filled with acidic juice, and its job is to break down proteins. This bag opens to let the food in, and then the lower muscle starts mixing the contents to ensure it is thoroughly combined with the juice. If the stomach is so full that it is stretched, this process cannot work well. If food enters the stomach without adequate chewing and digestion by saliva, the stomach cannot digest it properly.

Next, the food is pushed into the small intestine, where it is mixed with bile from the liver and pancreatic juice from the pancreas. The pancreatic juice digests proteins, fats, and carbohydrates; however, it needs the food to be processed by the previous parts of the digestive tract.

Finally, the food enters the large intestine, where bacteria can work through complex carbohydrates such as cellulose and other dietary fibers. If you have good bacteria in your gut, they will keep you healthy and help you get the most of your food. If you have pathogenic microorganisms, they might create gas and toxic byproducts.

It's important to understand that the digestive tract has to work every day, three or more times a day, processing everything that's put into it. Taoists believed that our digestive tract also helps digest our emotions, and that undigested emotions can upset the digestion process. Chewing slowly and mindfully, avoiding overfilling your stomach, and properly digesting your emotions (instead of holding them in your body) helps create a better environment for beneficial microorganisms.

Even though Taoists didn't know anything about antioxidants, they noticed the benefits of eating colorful, vibrant, fresh, and natural food. A simple rule I follow is to make sure I eat all five major colors of the five elements: red, yellow, white, blue, and green. Incidentally, many foods which are in this colorful category are fruits, berries, and vegetables which contain dietary fiber, antioxidants, and anti-inflammatory phytochemicals.

Let's Do This!

1. Select a time when you can eat slowly. You can imagine that you just went on a very expensive and highly sought-after spiritual health retreat, and this is one of the assignments you were given. You know it is important to make time for it.

2. Arrange your food on a pretty plate. Start with a small amount of food so you won't be tempted to rush through the meal. Sit down and relax. Look at your food and imagine all the people who had to work to bring this food to your table. Smile and send them your gratitude. Think of the earth and the sun and water and all the elements of nature that made it possible for this food to exist. Send them your gratitude. Smile into your food and into your own body. Breathe and relax.

3. Imagine a beautiful place in nature. Imagine gathering the energy of this place and taking it in with every bite.

4. Before you take the first bite, do your best to feel the energy of the food in front of you. This is something you will invite to enter your body. Look, listen, feel, and smell. Is it vibrant? Is it alive? Is it happy? Is it in alignment with your body? The answers might not come the first time you ask these questions, and that is OK. The more intentional you become about feeling the energy of your food, the more you will feel it. Eventually, knowing what is good for your body – and welcoming this goodness into your body — will become very easy and natural.

5. Put a small morsel of food in your mouth and start chewing mindfully. Feel how the taste changes and what part of your tongue feels the taste. Feel the pressure of your teeth and the sensations in your throat and stomach as you swallow. Make sure you generate enough saliva as you chew. Don't rush through it. You are working on improving your energy production process. Be intentional about it.

6. As you eat, notice your stomach. Finish eating when it is about ¾ full. After you finish eating, take a moment to place your palms on your heart and your abdomen, and send yourself good energy. Smile into your digestive tract and notice how the food feels in your body.

Taoist sages also developed a system of abdominal massage called Chi Nei Tsang. If there is a practitioner in your area trained in this method, I highly recommend it. It helps relax the intestines, releases the negative energy trapped in the gut, and improves digestion and movement. You can also learn to gently rub your abdominal area in a circular motion, do intentional abdominal breathing, and smile into your abdominal organs on your own.

Chapter 12

Becoming a Healer You
Were Always Meant to Be

I've come to believe that any challenges we are given in this life are there for a reason. If we decide to go on a personal healing journey, we have a chance to learn important lessons and let go of old patterns carried from generation to generation. My challenge was stuttering. It took me over 40 years to learn my lessons from this challenge.

As a child, I knew I was a person and that my thoughts, my joys, my sorrows, and my stories mattered.

And I was smart enough to notice that the majority of adults were unable to listen to me without:

1) Offering "helpful" advice on how to stop stuttering,
2) Becoming impatient,
3) Interrupting me and trying to finish my words for me.

I, on the other hand, believed that what I wanted to communicate was important and worthy of attention. I couldn't understand what was so difficult about just focusing on what I was saying, instead of being bothered by my special way of speaking.

When I became older and started studying the matters of the mind, I learned that many people, even those who never stuttered, feel unheard and unseen. The majority of people tend to jump to their judgements based on what they believe is important, instead of just paying attention to the person right in front of them.

Being a woman — especially a beautiful and sexually attractive woman — often comes with a particular struggle to be seen and heard as a person rather than being perceived as an object of appraisal and arousal by male listeners. Being an older woman with wrinkles and perhaps a few extra pounds in the "wrong" places often comes with a similar struggle with a more negative spin.

How difficult is it to see another person and listen without judgement? Not too difficult. And yet, it seems a very rare skill.

Emotional pain is pain. It is felt in our physical body. It creates a perfect storm of stress chemicals, and it affects us pretty much as any other pain.

Many women just accept the realities of living in the appraising and judgmental world. They might learn to constantly adjust to the opinions of others, and even go through the daily agony of self-criticism and comparing themselves to others. They do not realize how often all the other women they see who look so beautiful and confident on their social media pages are also trying very hard to present an edited and flattering image of themselves to win social likes and nods.

I used to believe that I needed to stop stuttering to finally be deserving of love. But here was the strangest thing: the more effort I put into trying to not stutter, the more I stuttered. The more I tried to present an image of myself I believed would win me likes and approving nods, the more insecure I felt about myself.

When I hired my first coach, the first question he asked was, "If you were to walk out of this door having achieved exactly what you came here for, what would it be like for you?"

I said without a moment's hesitation, "I want to stop stuttering."

Most clients who come to see me also answer with a statement which includes their problem.

"I want to lose some weight." "I want to stop being so anxious and stressed all the time." "I want to stop feeling like an impostor"

The next question was, "You want to stop stuttering and do what instead?"

"Hmm. I want to start speaking fluently?"

"And what would it get you?"

"Everything!"

"What specifically?"

Oh, boy, where do I begin...

I realized that I was so wrapped in my pain — which I believed stood between me and other people's approval — that I never asked myself these very simple question: "What do I want? How do I want to feel, sound, behave, and see myself?"

I never actually asked myself what I wanted to do with my voice, what I wanted to express, and who I would be without my pain.

Children dream boldly. Adults learn to be afraid of their dreams. Children know how to create space for their dreams. Adults let their dream space shrink, while their worry space expands and takes over.

My life changed when I decided to stop investing so much energy into my pain. Instead I started deliberately creating and growing my healing space - in my life, in my mind, and in my body.

The most important reason for creating your healing space and being very intentional about it is that you have control over how much space you allocate for healing. You do not have control over your pain space. Pain builds by itself. All it needs is your energy and attention. But your healing space is your creation. You can intentionally build, expand, and decorate it.

As I progressed in my healing journey, I remembered more and more something I knew as a child: I'm a child of the Universe. I'm divine. I'm a healer in my heart.
I had to look my pain straight in the face and say, "I might experience a terrible discomfort in that moment of pain. But I'm not it."

When I learned to focus on my inner energy, my body, my spirit, and my soul — my true energy self — it changed everything.

Many of my clients have healing gifts inside. They are born healers. I teach them how to create the space for healing.

Healing requires a space filled with love. Healing requires quietness and softness. It cannot be done in a hurry. It cannot be done in a tight, busy, overwhelmed body. Healing requires pure clean radiant energy.

When you start identifying with the spiritual (or energy) part of yourself, when you become intentional about creating a healing space, and when you truly begin welcoming in a healer's identity, it changes everything.

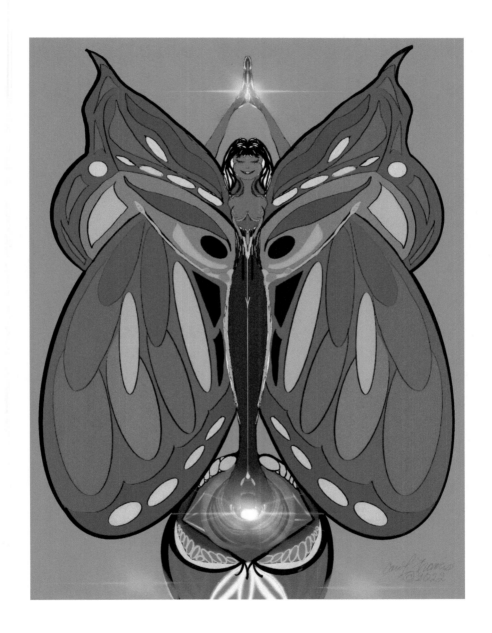

Chapter 13

Healing the Inner Child: Return to Playfulness

Dangling his legs in the cool clear water on the shores of Rattlesnake Lake, my son casually remarked, "You know, you cannot fix broken glass with a hammer."

"WHAT?"

"You know. If you try, it will only keep breaking it more."

He was right, as usual. Applying force to a fragile broken thing will only break it more. I wish I had known that way earlier.

Many people know that it is important to heal the inner child. And they usually want to heal her fast. They want to fix this darn inner child ASAP, and get on with their busy lives.

They want to fix broken glass with a hammer in one mighty blow.

Many clients are surprised when they realize that forcing themselves to heal only hurts more. But when they relax and listen, without being in a hurry, they can learn a lot from their inner child.

The other day, I was teaching my son how to use hypnosis to relieve a headache, "Notice the color of this feeling. Notice it's shape. What else do you notice?"

And he said, "There is this infinite space inside my head. It is bigger than the Universe."

My son asked me once, "Mom, why do adults keep trying to change their children?"

I thought about it and said earnestly, "Because they imagine how they want their children to be, and then they want to change them into the children they have imagined."

My son thought about it and said, "I think if they want their real children to behave how they have imagined they should behave, they should just get themselves imaginary children, and imagine them exactly as they have imagined their children to be."

The more I work with clients, the more I am amazed at the deep wisdom their inner child possesses. Once they stop hurrying their inner child and trying to force them to behave how they think they should behave, they can get quiet and deep within themselves to finally connect, listen, and learn.

Old Ways Won't Open New Doors

Many people who struggle to become vital do not realize that the modern obsession with personal health, happiness, and longevity is a relatively new trend. In the past, a human body was considered a resource which was used to serve the needs of other people. Even the wealthiest and most powerful people usually were expected to serve the King or the Emperor, and give up their life if needed. As a result, most cultural conditioning has been focused on preparing a person for their service to society and other people. Resources of the physical body of an individual were there for a very simple reason - to be used. When these resources were gone, the body was simply discarded and replaced by a new one. A fallen soldier could be easily replaced by a new recruit. An elderly and infirm farmer could let his children work in the field. A woman who died in childbirth could be replaced by a new wife. This arrangement would work really well if not for human emotions. Since the dawn of time, human emotions have defied rule and reason, and have remained the unconquerable force which prevented society from becoming a collection of well-functioning human robots.

As we know from the works of Shakespeare and other great writers, even though much effort has been invested into training children and adults to suppress and dismiss their emotions, the human heart will resist any attempts to tame it. Despite the fear of punishment, public shaming, and even death, human beings keep falling in love. They keep feeling compassion, curiosity, and various desires, even when contradicted by existing rules and customs.

Historically, people have been trained to use socially acceptable ways to entertain their senses and discharge emotional tension. Anger and aggression could be satisfied through watching violent shows such as gladiator fights or more modern sports; sorrow and unhappiness could be drowned in alcohol; and unbridled joy could be safely expressed through dancing or singing. Those people who failed to control, suppress, or safely discharge their emotions were severely punished: tortured, burned, beheaded, whipped, stoned to death, imprisoned, or thrown into horrific mental institutions. Women had to become especially good at hiding, suppressing, or disowning their own emotions since throughout most of history they were considered the property of men. A lot of social conditioning for women was directed at fostering obedience, servitude, and self-sacrifice, as well as suppressing their sexuality and desire for pleasure.

Today, many people want to be happy and healthy, and to live a long and fulfilling life. Paradoxically, this desire for happiness and fulfillment creates a lot of unhappiness and the feeling of being unfulfilled, which negatively impacts health and longevity. People know what they want but they do not know how to get it. Many modern women know they deserve to be happy, confident, and powerful, but they don't know how to escape the prison of their own social conditioning which keeps them feeling stressed, overwhelmed, overworked, ashamed, guilty, subservient, inferior, and restricted.

Despite all the advances of modern psychology, we still have to deal with the result of eons of social conditioning ingrained into our neurology and thinking. People are still expected to be able to control the expression of their emotions through willpower, guilt, shame, fear, and anger. Even among mental health specialists there is still very little understanding of the physiological effects of emotions, and the connection between physical health and emotions. The human heart still remains a mystery and an unconquerable force.

Taoist wisdom is so valuable today because Taoist Masters have had thousands of years of study and practice in the field of human happiness, health, and longevity. Long before modern scientific discoveries, they recognized the power and true nature of human emotions as energy generated in the physical body. Just like Western scientists learned to harness the power of electromagnetic energy through technological devices, Taoist Masters developed the technology for working with the energy of human emotions, including the most powerful forces of nature – love and sexual energy.

Taoist practices offer a truly unique approach to happiness, health, and longevity because they are focused on working with the physiology and chemistry of human emotions in the physical body. While Western psychology traditionally considered the mind and body as separate, Taoists recognized that emotions are generated and stored in physical organs. They have the same nature as other expressions of energy in the body such as the heartbeat, breathing, muscle tension, etc. They noticed that certain emotions increased vitality while others made the body weak and sick. They also discovered that sick organs generated more negative emotions, while healthy and vibrant organs generated more vibrant and uplifting feelings.

Today, modern science focuses more and more attention to the health effects of emotions. Since people want to live longer and be happier, it is important to recognize that stress and suppressed negative emotions are emerging as the main cause of diseases associated with aging and mortality.

Taoist practices also offer a unique approach to gender equality. Because both men and women could become students of the Tao and reach mastery, Taoist practices accumulated a wealth of practical knowledge about the specifics of female physiology. It was considered neither superior nor inferior to male physiology – just different. As a result, spiritual practices of the Tao include sexual practices focused on mutual pleasure, an intimate soul connection, and fulfilment for both partners — not just male satisfaction.

In the sacred feminine vitality practices of the Tao, emotions were not a nuisance; they were powerful forces which move and animate the physical body and give power and vibrancy to the mind and spirit. A female body was cherished as a treasury of spiritual gifts, and her womb was revered as a portal through which new souls pass from the spiritual realm to the embodied existence. Rather than seeing a human body as merely a resource to use or a property to possess, Taoist Masters believed that we are spiritual beings having a human experience. Therefore the purpose of life was to learn from this experience, gain wisdom, and develop one's own spiritual essence. This was believed to be possible only while having a physical body. This made health and longevity very important – the longer one lives, the longer one can learn, experience, and develop spiritually. On this path, men and women were considered equal, and the difference in their practices was dictated by real and important differences in their physiology — not their hierarchy on the ladder of social values.

A Drawing On a Wall

One of my early memories from my childhood is me, drawing…on the wall in our only room in our Soviet-era large communal flat. I am alone in the room and I am painting with my mother's makeup pencils. Imagine that! Oh, how angry she was! In the Soviet Union, makeup wasn't easy to find; the stores were empty. And I imagine to her a set of beautiful makeup pencils was a real treasure. I certainly ruined it.

This memory was stuck in my mind as one of the examples of my terrible misbehaving. I knew I was a difficult child. And this was just one of the examples of what I believed were senseless and stupid mischiefs in which I so frequently engaged.

As I was growing up I put a lot of effort into becoming a "good girl," and developed a strong fear of anything improper. I became a very serious young lady, and then a very serious not-so-young lady. The only times when my fun would come bubbling to the surface was when I was drunk. And (I'm sorry to admit) this happened a lot. I needed either good goofy company, or a good goofy movie, or some vodka to unleash my funny side.

I remember one time I was getting ready for a family celebration, and my partner at that time said, "Anna, we're going to have fun. Look at your face — you're way too serious!"

I felt hurt!

I was more than 50 years old when I learned to laugh, smile, and play again without needing alcohol (which I stopped drinking), or any other special stimulation.

One life-changing experience was a hypnotherapy session. My hypnotherapist took me all the way back before I made the dreaded drawing on the wall. He asked me how I felt in my body right before the mischief.

All of a sudden, in hypnosis, I could feel, see, smell, and hear this moment so vibrantly. I felt alive. I felt I smiled with my entire body. I felt curious and playful. It was fun to press the pencil to the blank wall and see a line appearing, as if by magic. Then another line, and another, forming patterns, taking different shapes. I was the creator. I felt my magnificence. There was joy flowing through me.

For many men, playfulness in a woman is a sign of vitality. One reason a middle-aged man might fall hopelessly in love with a much younger woman is not just the smoothness of her skin or beauty of her body. It's this bubbly, flowing, mischievous, joyful energy, which excites and ignites a man's desire.

Even if you don't have any seduction plans, even if you are single and love it, don't you think you owe it to yourself to reclaim your playful spirit?

Here's what playfulness will do for you:

- You will feel lighter in your heart and body.
- You will feel more alive, and buzzing with sensual energy.
- You will be much more alluring and attractive.
- You will look younger and more radiant.
- Your skin will glow and your eyes will shine.
- You will start having much more fun, and experience more pleasure during lovemaking.
- You will give more pleasure to others.

The primary reason so many women stop being playful — and forget how to be lighter and have more fun — is some negative experience from their childhood.

Think about it. When is a child most likely to get into trouble? When exercising their curiosity, exploring their creativity, and searching for fun. You never got into trouble for doing your house chores on time, or completing all your homework. Your playful, goofy, fun actions and choices are the ones which ended up badly.

Children are naturally playful. Adults become way too serious. But look at animals. Dogs often play until a very old age. It's not aging itself which extinguishes the playful spirit. It's social conditioning and fear.

Many women have negative experiences in their sexual life. Many women experience sexual trauma and abuse. Many women grow up being ashamed of their sexuality. This is the soil in which playfulness doesn't grow.

It's time to change this. Playfulness is your birthright. It ignites your creativity, relieves stress, and adds fire and flow to your sexual organs. It's time to return to playfulness.

Taoists developed many powerful meditations for releasing negative energies. The simplest one is the Inner Smile, which we discussed earlier. Taoists believed that universal love is the ultimate detoxifier. The Inner Smile helps melt negative emotions through the power of unconditional love. Do it often and let your love melt all the old beliefs, perceptions, and negative conditioning. Let love win.

Another great exercise is laughter. Taoists had their own version of the Laughter Yoga. One of my favorite exercises is called the Laughing Baby.

Lie on your back. Lift your legs and arms in the air like a happy dog rolling in the grass. Shake your arms and legs and laugh, laugh, laugh. Reclaim your joy.

Making art is a wonderful way to call back your creativity. Don't worry about being perfect. Mess around. Allow yourself to just play with colors and shapes.

Take improvisation classes. Dance. Sing. Make faces in front of the mirror.

And above all, keep practicing lightening up and releasing heavy and toxic negative energy from your body. You are a laughing animal. Your creativity needs laughter and fun just as flowers need water.

Women are like earth. Women's laughter and playfulness are like flowers brightening up the face of the Earth.

Return to playfulness. Free your fun.

For me, the return to fun was like coming home to myself. It was refreshing, buzzy, tingling, and exhilarating.

When you lighten up, you become delightful. And if you wish to use your playfulness for seduction, you will soon realize its surprising powers.

The Unconscious Mind and Your Energy

Sometimes people ask me whether we should refer to the automatic patterns of the deep mind as "the subconscious mind" or "the unconscious mind." This is how I view it.

It is subconscious, because there are structures underlying all our conscious thoughts, words, and actions. They are energy idea-forms which most people are unaware of, but which determine what we say, what we do, and how we feel. They are your mental images, inner talk, and body sensations. They have intensity, location, and relationships with each other. They are energy codes from past experiences — and even past lives. They are energy codes from other people, which might be useful or destructive. Because most people are unaware of these subconscious energy structures, we can call them unconscious. They are not in our consciousness, but you can access them in a meditative, hypnotic state. So it is both subconscious and unconscious. A lot of what goes on in your brain and body neurology happens beneath the surface of language and conscious thinking.

Words are, by their nature, surface structures. We feel something, we think something, we remember events and sensations, and we wrap words around them. We say "I love you" to express a tsunami of feelings which sweeps through our body, mind, and spirit, making us temporarily insane. "I love you" is on the surface. The raving raw madness of the feeling is much deeper.

In order to access this deeper level, you need to ask yourself how you feel this energy and how it moves in your body. There are layers and layers of subconscious structures, and the deeper you go the more unconscious they become. And very deep down, on the physical body level, there are neuronal connections and the flow of electromagnetic energy.

As one of my teachers said, "Our behaviors are wired into our body neuro-illogically." It is the job of your conscious mind to find logic, justification, and reasons. But on the deepest level, all you have are the energy patterns wired into your body. Taoist Masters did not use words such as the "subconscious" or "unconscious" mind, but through meditative practices they discovered that everything is energy. When you learn how to move and transform your real and raw energy, you are no longer afraid of being alive or feeling big feelings in your real physical body. These feelings become your personal power, and your personal liberation from unhealthy and restrictive cultural conditioning. However, you have to learn how to use this power and take full responsibility for it. If you've seen the *Spiderman* movies, you might remember this quote: "With great power comes great responsibility." Ultimately, we are responsible for our body and our energy, just as we are responsible for our planet Earth.

How to Seduce Yourself Playfully

If you want to be seductive, sensual, alluring, and exciting, you need to know how to seduce yourself.

What is seduction? Have you ever been seduced?

For example, have your even been seduced into buying something you weren't planning on buying? How did it happen?

How did French courtesan Ninon de L'Enclos seduce men when she was 80 years old?

The truth about seduction is it's not logical. No amount of logic can create that special feeling of desire, the overpowering YES in your body which silences the voice of reason. When something or somebody activates the YES response, it's visceral, it's sensual, and it's irresistible. Oh, YES — I want it!

I suggest you learn how to seduce yourself.

How do you need to talk to yourself to feel the tantalizing feeling of YES in your body?

Yes to self-care. Yes to your Yoni egg practice. Yes to the daily watering of your garden!

How do you need to feel inside in order to want — really want — to have a vital, vibrant, sensual body?

Master Chia gave a precious gift to Western women. He revealed and clearly explained the secret practices of Sexual Energy Alchemy Feminine Vitality developed by the ancient Taoist masters. If you are a Western woman and you're introduced to these practices for the first time, what are you going to do with them? Are you going to read this book, put it away, and forget about it? Are you going to buy a Yoni egg, play with it for a few days, and then put it in a drawer and let it gather dust for the next decade? Maybe you'll take it out again in 10 years and look at it with a guilty feeling? Then put it back in a drawer and forget about it for good? Or are you going to take charge of your sexual energy and feminine vitality? Are you going to neglect your sexual organs? Or are you going to become a fearless champion of your body, dedicated to uplifting its vitality, rejuvenating its energy, and reinvigorating its sexuality?

Women's bodies are like earth. They produce beautiful flowers when they are soft, loved, and replenished with flowing energy. Start taking care of your body. It's very simple. If you do nothing, the natural course will be deterioration, weakening, and loss of vitality. To enjoy your body and your sexual vitality longer, you have to do something different.

I have been blessed to have experienced many seasons of a woman's life. I've been a little girl, teenage girl, young woman, and maturing woman. I entered the unique season of transition when I stepped over the 50-year-old threshold, and I'm there now.

For many women, 50 is a time of awakening and healing. When they answer the call, it can dramatically alter the way they age; creating a special, radiant, and strong ageless appearance and inner state. I love this season. I see it as a unique opportunity to start investing into bettering myself for myself, without feeling selfish. Think about it. If my body is healthy and strong — not just now, but for years and years ahead — I'm not the only one who benefits. My family, friends, and clients will benefit as well. Since I've turned 50, taking care of my body has had to become my priority, and it's taken an investment of time and energy. And the most important component of keeping my body strong and healthy has been maintaining the energy of my mind. I can no longer afford to waste my life energy on inner conflicts and destructive emotions. I can no longer afford to use alcohol, food, or constant busy-ness to run away from pain and uncomfortable thoughts. I can no longer afford to beat myself up, loathe myself, or discount my needs. It's time to gear up for a journey into the next season of life.

Think about it. Your skin and body will age. But the energy of your mind — the light of your soul — can stay young forever. You can even take this youthful and vibrant energy with you as your soul transitions out of this earthly plane.

It seems so many people see life after 50 as a slow descend into decay, deterioration, and dying. And that might be true for the body. But the beauty of the human mind and spirit is that we have a choice. We can allow it to decay and deteriorate; or continue growing, evolving, and developing. And here's what is truly amazing: By developing our mind we can help our body to be stronger, healthier, and more vibrant. Life after 50 can mean another 20, 30, 40, or even 50 years. And it can be a time of new blossoming.

Your most important relationship is with yourself. How many times have you heard that? Here's what it means.

You are stuck with yourself for the duration of your time on this planet. There is no divorcing yourself. You cannot move out.

You completely depend on yourself for everything. You have to move your own body, make your own decisions, groom and dress yourself, and put food into your mouth.

Your body is the house in which you live with yourself. It is pretty resilient. You can fix some damage, you can replace selected parts when they break, and you can make it last longer if you take good care of it. But you are not getting another one. This is it!

But there is something even more important: the chemistry of your body. You can have love chemistry or fear chemistry. Compassion chemistry or hate chemistry. Laughter chemistry or sadness chemistry. There are an infinite variety of chemicals you can create in your body. You have your own personal alchemist inside you.

Your energy is your message to the world. It enters the room before you do, and it speaks before you utter a word. It radiates through your skin, touches every person in the room, and influences people's emotional states.

Peaceful, tranquil, and well-balanced energy is comforting.

Excitement and passion are stimulating.

Playfulness and sensuality are enticing.

Compassion and unconditional love are healing.

As your body gets older, your mind and spirit can continue to grow and develop. The elevation of your vibrations; release of toxic, heavy, and painful emotional energy; and continuous replenishment, regeneration, and restoration of your positive energy can continue for the rest of your life. As you elevate your vibrations, your new ageless beauty is created.

Chapter 14

Making it Real:
Sacred Feminine Vitality Kung Fu

Work hard, they say. Then when you retire, you will have enough wealth to do all the things you always wanted to do. How many people bought into this story, only to arrive at their promised golden age and realize they are no longer able to do all the things they wanted to do? How many people realized that a healthy bank account attached to a sick and desperate body is a doctor's dream and a personal nightmare?

I decided to change the picture. I set up a goal to be active and independent, and enjoying life at the age of 100+.

Is it possible? I don't know. But I know that there are people who continue working, playing, and having fun at the age of 90 and beyond.

To live actively and continue having fun we need three treasures:

1. A healthy body
2. A sane and active mind
3. Balanced emotions for loving connections

If we sacrifice our health, suffocate our spirit, and poison our mind, aging is no fun. And money is not going to fix it.

I have lived on this planet long enough to learn that a strong and healthy body has way more opportunities and abilities to enjoy life's pleasures. All kinds of fun, all kinds of learning opportunities, and all kinds of ways to earn a living are available to those who are healthy, strong, and possess all their mental faculties. So does it really make sense to postpone those pleasures until some uncertain time in the future when we have finally saved enough money? Or is it better to allocate time, energy, and financial resources to maintaining our own body, energy, and mental resources?

I know my answers. I know what I want. It is not just a long life that I desire and crave. I dream that when the last breath comes, whenever this might be, it will be a breath of deep satisfaction and contentment from appreciating the fullness and beauty of life.

Practicing Self-Love for Life

Knowledge is grand, but if you do not have a daily practice to grow what you want to create, you might merely end up with a head full of words.

My Universal Healing Tao teacher, Master Chia, once said:
"People ask me what is my secret. I have three secrets. First, I know energy is real, and I teach you the Inner Alchemy Qigong. I give you a real energy practice. Second, I practice a lot what I teach. Third, I teach a lot what I practice."

As we know from neuroscience, practice rewires our neurology and builds new and more effective neural pathways. This is why, just like Master Chia, I practice what I teach, I teach what I practice, and I love what I teach. I believe that if you practice any meditation method long enough, you will get results. But most people do not practice long enough because they run into resistance. The nature of resistance is that it might be quite stubborn, and it might take a long time to get past it. Traditionally, resistance is dissolved through years of diligent practice. Being over 50, I couldn't wait 20 years. I wanted to be happy, healthy, and peaceful as soon as possible. Fortunately, I discovered a secret ingredient — which I knew I had — but had never thought about adding to my Taoist Inner Alchemy and Qigong practice.

It all started with a client who wanted to learn the Emotional Alchemy of the Tao from me. She was hindered by emotions emerging every time she tried to meditate. Being a hypnotherapist, it was very natural for me to start using hypnotherapy to help her make sense of (and make peace with) these feelings. We both loved the results, so I started using hypnosis with all my clients. And of course, I started adding hypnosis to my own meditations.

In one of his books, Master Chia has a story about a time when a group of scientists measured his brain activity while he was doing the foundational meditation of the Tao - The Inner Smile. When the results appeared on their screens, they were shocked. "Master Chia is sleeping and talking to us at the same time!" I can confirm this is true. I had a similar experience when I went to a hypnotherapy conference, and had a chance to attach myself to a machine which displayed a person's brain activity in colors on a computer screen. Guess what? When I put myself in a light hypnotic trance and started doing the Inner Smile, the lady who took the measurements was shocked. "Wait a minute! What are you doing with your brain? You look like you are asleep but you are not!" I didn't have decades of practice like Master Chia did, but my brain was already doing something very unusual.

I learned something very important. I have to practice what I know in order to have the confidence to teach it. I have to know how these practices affect my mind and body in order to have the confidence to share them with others. And I have to love what I practice in order to teach what I love. I know from my own practice how good it feels when my body finally opens to energies and rich sensations. I know how good it feels to have my life force flowing through my body freely. I know how good it feels to be at peace and love own body. I know how good it feels to feel beautiful and have a glow on my face.

I know how good it feels to have smiling sunshine in my heart even in the darkest of times. I practice what I teach and I love what I practice. I hope you will fall in love with these practices, and will keep infusing your practice with smiling, loving, sunshine energy for your enjoyment and benefit.

Life-Long Benefits

I used to dislike seeing photographs of myself. Now I enjoy seeing myself.

It is me in my own physical body. How wonderful it is!

And besides — I am a responsible body owner now. I love my body and take good care of it. I know that my body is completely dependent on me. I know my body won't move unless I move it. I know I have to feed my body. My body can't receive fresh, clean, wholesome, vibrant foods unless I put them in my mouth.

I am aware that my body will have to process all the neurochemicals, hormones, and inflammatory molecules produced in response to my thinking. So I am gentle with my body, and fill it with healing thoughts.

Loving my body makes a lot of sense to me. It is alive. It is intelligent. It has the ability to feel pain and pleasure. And it is in my care. My head might be in the clouds, but my body keeps my feet on the ground. The more I love my body, the more it loves me back, allowing me to experience life's vibrancy and joy.

When I started learning Taoist energy alchemy and Qigong, I didn't know where it would take me. Over the years it has transformed my body, healed my mind, and regenerated my soul. It opened me to the joy and pleasure of being in my body. Sometimes I do not want to get up in the morning and practice. Then I think about my 109-year-old self and ask, "What can I do for you today so you grow stronger and happier?"

And I know the answer: "Keep investing in yourself. Keep taking care of this body, this temple. Every day, invest a little. It will bring rich dividends over time."

Here are just some of the benefits I received from my daily practice:

- Stopped needing (and therefore drinking) alcohol
- Lost 40 pounds without dieting or worrying about my weight
- Built a strong and resilient body through daily Qigong exercises
- Stopped abusing and neglecting myself and started relating to myself with love
- Retired my inner critic and replaced her with my inner coach, who is much more encouraging, gentle, and supportive of my dreams and goals
- Stopped being afraid of aging and started making sure my body is able to deal with the challenges of getting older
- Started looking younger and more radiant
- Developed confidence through self-love
- Stopped being afraid of my emotions and other people's judgements
- Regained my playfulness and inner peace
- Started feeling lighter, brighter, and happier in my body
- Stopped trying to change other people and started enjoying experiencing a variety of opinions, ways of living, and perspectives

Invest In Yourself Daily

Ancient Taoist practices were built for practicing. In China there is the term "Kung Fu," which Westerners have learned to associate with a particular style of martial art. However, kung fu — or gong fu — simply means "good work." It's an art of daily disciplined work, which has its own reward built in. You do not wait to feel good when you drop an extra 20 pounds. You do not wait to be happy when a perfect lover waltzes into your life. You do not wait to feel good when your business is blossoming.

You feel good every day when you do your daily practices. You feel good because you are doing kung fu.

I invite you to start thinking about your vitality practices as your personal kung fu.

Smile into your practice. Smile into your past and your future. Smile into your imperfections, and love your journey.

Think about something you love doing and do well. You do it so well, it's no longer a struggle or a chore. It's your time to do something for yourself. To relax and to connect with your true self. This is your kung fu.

I started progressing in my Taoist vitality practices when I decided to become an instructor. One problem was it included passing a series of tests supervised by Master Chia himself and his senior instructors.

I had to be able to teach the basics of the Tao, such as the Inner Smile and the Microcosmic Orbit.

I had to pass my Iron Shirt test, which consisted of maintaining a standing meditation for 30 minutes, and then retaining my rooting and centering so well I could continue standing even after being pushed quite hard by my instructors.

I also had to pass a test on my knowledge of the Healing Love and Sexual Energy Alchemy of the Tao.

I knew I had to practice.

I started waking up every day at 6 am, and doing my Qigong and Taoist meditation practices for 90 minutes. I would do another (shorter) practice session mid-day. And another in the evening.

It was only then I discovered what my instructors meant when they were talking about kung fu.

Day by day I developed my mastery, my confidence, and my inner power. Day by day it felt better and better to move my body, to connect to myself, and to feel energy flowing.

This practice developed my body, elevated my vibrancy, and brought me levels of confidence and authentic connections I never imagined were possible.

And yes, I passed my tests!

Below is a sample program you can do every day. Feel free to modify it according to your personality and style.

Morning

Start your day with the Inner Smile meditation. Make your Yoni egg practice part of your morning ritual. It becomes very easy when you can do it standing up. You just wash your egg, insert it (you can do it in the shower), and do the practice for five minutes. Then you take the egg out, wash it, and put it back in its place.

Use the morning to breathe into your ovaries and uterus. If you no longer have a uterus, breathe into the sacred womb energy space.

Morning also is a perfect time to do your Qigong exercises. Even five minutes in the morning will keep you energized and flowing.

Remember your bamboo hitter and breast massage.

You do not need to do every practice in this book every day. Choose the one you like, and the one you feel your body needs. Adjust your practice to the amount of time you have.

During the Day

Take minibreaks to relax and smile into your body and your yoni. You can practice pulling up your anus and perineum any time during the day. You can practice mindfulness and slowing down to be in the moment. You can do breathing exercises and simple Qigong. Remember that your spine needs to move in order for your brain to be healthy and sharp. Standing up and doing simple Qigong will help your brain detox and receive more blood and oxygen.

Before Sleep

Help your body unwind by using heart-to-sexual organ breathing, and the Microcosmic Orbit meditation.

You can finish the day with The Inner Smile Emotional Detox meditation. As you go from organ to organ, smile loving sunshine into them, and imagine releasing all the dark and cloudy energy from them. It is important to form your intention to release. You can practice releasing negative energy while standing barefoot on the ground. Let the emotion arise, smile into it without judgement, and let it go into the earth. Let the golden light of earth Chi come into your body, and feel peaceful and calm.

If you are curious about more ways to release negative energy and emotional detox practices, please refer to other books by Master Chia such as *The Six Healing Sounds* and *Fusion of the Five Elements*.

Take good care of your feminine organs. Learn to touch them. Learn to use your Yoni egg. Learn to seduce yourself and pamper yourself. Learn to smile into your body, and take the time to release negative and toxic emotions.

Your body is in your care. Your sexual energy is your creative and magical spiritual power.

Imagine your body blossoming. Imagine your body becoming resilient and strong. And imagine reclaiming your sacred feminine vitality daily.

Your Body Is Your Garden

Once upon a time there was a gardener who loved his beautiful garden, yet sometimes he resented watering and feeding the plants. A long time ago, when he had just become a gardener, he felt excited and enthusiastic about taking care of it. But as time passed and his initial passion faded, he started feeling trapped with all those chores. He started thinking about other dreams he wanted to pursue, and wondered if he gave his garden too high a priority.

As the flowers kept wilting and demanded more attention, it became increasingly difficult for him to drag himself out of bed every morning to do his garden chores.

One day when he was watering the plants and feeling even more resentful than usual, he suddenly noticed how with every watering, the flowers looked more and more beautiful, glowing, and smiling. He unexpectedly realized how good it felt knowing he had something to do with it. He was responsible for these smiles and this glow. He thought of how much more enjoyment he would feel as his garden kept blossoming, becoming even more beautiful and vibrant.

And ever since that day, the gardener kept finding more creative ways to take good care of his garden, taking great pride in how beautiful and vibrant his flowers looked.

He found his passion rekindled. He started leaping out of bed every morning to take care of his garden with great joy and enthusiasm.

He also discovered when he really was too busy or too tired to water the plants, his garden still looked beautiful and vibrant.

With daily care, the plants developed deep roots and much more resilience.

So the gardener now had more freedom and more time to pursue his dreams, while having enough energy and vigor to keep enjoying his beautiful garden.

Comfort vs. Growth

People want life to be easy and comfortable
They do not realize
Life becomes easier and more comfortable
With every storm we have been through
And survived
And learned
New skills
New lessons
And discovered
Resources
And powers
And strength
We had no idea we had
People want relationships to be easy and comfortable
They do not realize
That the best relationship
Is when two people have courage to become real with each other
And survive
And burn their path through obstacles
And allow their love to transform them
To become one
People want to be normal
They do not realize
That their pain, their trauma, their challenges and weirdness
Are pure magic
Waiting to be mastered and shared
Your body is a sacred vessel for your energy
Your energy feeds and transforms your body
Do not be afraid of fire
Be the fire
When you master your energy
You master your fire
Your master your magic
You master your relationships
You master your life

Conclusion

As Above as Below:
The Ecology of Consciousness

In 1983, Hawaiian sugar plantation owners frustrated with rats devastating their sugar cane fields came up with a "brilliant" idea. They decided that a solution to all their trouble would be the mongoose: a sleek, fast, and furry animal native to India.

Indeed, who better than a mongoose? A perfect hunter who can fit inside rat tunnels, and is vicious and voracious enough to take on a rat would surely be the solution. So 72 mongooses were shipped from Jamaica and distributed to Hawaii, Maui, Oahu, and Molokai. (Fortunately, none were brought to Kauai.) There was one thing that sugar plantation owners failed to realize. Mongooses (indeed commendable hunters) are active during the day. Rats (indeed commendable pests) are active at night. Mongooses have no natural predators on the Hawaiian islands, and they themselves are predators with an appetite for birds (and their eggs), lizards, geckos, and many other juicy and crunchy invertebrates. A female mongoose can start reproducing at the age of 10 months and can have three to four litters a year. Do you see the problem? If you don't, come visit the Big Island. The mongooses are now omnipresent.

The introduction of mongooses to Hawaii was an epic failure which led to the decimation (or even disappearance) of many varieties of endemic birds. A unique species of Hawaiian goose, the Nene, a ground-nesting bird extremely vulnerable to predators, was brought to the brink of extinction by mongooses. What sugar plantation owners failed to consider was ecology.

Today we have ecological apparel, food, resorts, and retreats. Many people, when they hear the word "ecological" or see "eco-friendly" on labels, instantly think of something good for the body and the environment. However, ecology by itself is neither good nor bad. It's a branch of science which considers how living organisms (including humans) affect each other and their environment.

The Merriam-Webster dictionary defines ecology as:

1. a branch of science concerned with the interrelationship of organisms and their environments.
2. the totality or pattern of relations between organisms and their environment.

On the evening of August 22nd, 2021, I did a full moon meditation before I went to sleep. It was a special full moon, the blue moon, and I was on a magical vacation on the Big Island of Hawaii. This explains why I woke up with a clear voice in my head saying, "Now, let's consider the ecology of consciousness." Just this one phrase, spoken with an air of utmost significance.

When my dream mind speaks to me, especially once in a blue moon, I listen.

There is no shortage of health-related information. However, for many people it's often remarkably difficult to adopt a lifestyle they know will help them maintain vitality and vibrant health. The reality is that rather than plan their life for vibrancy and longevity, most people just go day to day dealing with one pressing problem after another, accepting whatever consequences come from their choices and behaviors. Being intentional about maintaining one's own vitality is not always easy, and it requires a major mindset shift toward more ecological thinking.

The sugar plantation owners had a pressing need. They wanted to find a way to reduce losses caused by rats, and they needed it fast. However, while coming up with a logical solution for this problem, they missed a lot of relevant data because they failed to take into account the interrelation of other species present on the island. They even failed to notice the true nature of the interrelation between mongooses and rats. A failure is just evidence that whatever we thought we knew and understood was not accurate enough to get us the outcome we wanted.

The Unconscious Mind Is a Wonderful Servant, but a Terrible Master

Canadian writer Robin S. Sharma said that the mind is a wonderful servant, but a terrible master. This is very true about the unconscious mind. As the conscious mind comes up with needs, desires, and problems, the unconscious mind does its best to find the quickest, easiest, and most energy-efficient solution. The unconscious mind lives in the present, and therefore might not always be aware of the long-term consequences of our choices — unless we bring them to its attention.

For example, what would give you a feeling of vitality and power right now? It might be an inspirational post on social media, a YouTube video, a compliment, a glass of wine, or a piece of chocolate cake. It might be buying a new exercise program which will end up on your bookshelf covered with dust. These solutions offer a quick relief, but they do not increase your vitality in the long run. And if you consider the ecology of every choice, you might discover that some of those choices will eventually deplete your energy and diminish your vitality.

The science of ecology deals with real and physical organisms (human and non-human) interacting in their real and physical environment. But ecology as a natural reality also includes something much less tangible: the realities of the mind. In every physical relationship, there are needs, wants, and desires of the individual minds, shaped by their individual cultures, and powered by their individual emotions. Therefore, when we consider the ecology of human consciousness, we have to consider human ideas, beliefs, cultures and, most importantly, language, which shapes, defines, contains, and conveys them.

We also need to consider emotions evoked not only by natural factors such as hunger, danger, or sexual desire, but also by words and ideas. These forces of nature are not as obvious, and might not be as easy to measure as the predatory path of the mongoose, but they greatly affect the ecosystems of our minds and bodies. They also affect the bigger ecosystems of our families, workplaces, relationships, societies and, ultimately, the ecosystem of our planet.

The main advantage of the human mind is that we can become aware of our own thinking patterns. We can get curious about the laws which govern our own consciousness, body, and environment, as well as learn how other minds work, and decide how to use this knowledge. The main pitfall of the human mind is that it tends to automate behaviors and responses, and then justify their existence as if they were immutable laws of the Universe.

How the Solution to a Problem Might Become a Problem

Most people want to feel good, whatever "feeling good" means to them. Most people want to stay alive, whatever "staying alive" means to them. Most people need to go to work and obey societal norms and rules. We cannot ignore this. It is very natural for people to focus on the immediate and most pressing problems they need to solve, pushing other problems which they consider less urgent or less important out of their awareness.

Too often what gets pushed to the back burner is the health and vitality of our own body. But just as a house of cards crumbles once a card from the base is removed — and just as humans cannot survive without their planet — the mighty tower of our personality and higher consciousness simply ceases to exist without the support of the body. We might like or dislike our bodies, but we cannot live without them. Just like our planet, our bodies are resourceful and adaptable, but it doesn't mean their resources cannot be depleted or exhausted.

Our bodies and minds are ecosystems, and the truth about ecosystems is that when they start to crumble and deteriorate, all parts of the system eventually feel the effects. The more you are aware of interrelations within the ecological system, the more you can help it thrive. And we cannot do it from the same mindset and culture which created the problem.

Becoming the Change You Wish to See in This World

Political ethicist Mahatma Ghandi said, "You must be the change you wish to see in the world."

We just recently started to fully realize that ideas, beliefs, and other thought-forms inhabiting our mental landscape are very real, and they uniquely influence our emotional landscape and the environment of our physical bodies. They are what they are, and it's best to study them, be aware of them, and learn how to work with them rather than fear, condemn, and ignore them.

If you want to develop more ecological thinking, you have to learn to step into a neutral observing state and gather data until you start seeing the patterns of interrelations. You have to step out of the ideological environment of your family traditions, your personal history, and your culture to start seeing what is really there, and start building your understanding of the ecology of consciousness. This is why hypnosis and meditation are so important — because they are very good at creating this relaxed and neutral state.

You do not have to have a Master's in Ecological Sciences to determine if an ecosystem is thriving or dying. Some of the most important characteristics are vibrancy, variety, and abundance. It's very similar with the ecology of consciousness. A healthy vital body with a life force flowing abundantly can support and balance a wide variety of emotional energies, allowing vibrant sensuality and youthful vigor.

No amount of money, entertainment, sex, or recreational drugs can replace the sense of joy, pleasure, playfulness, and aliveness flowing through the skin, shining from the eyes, and radiating through every pore of one's being.

The truth is that minds and bodies do not exist in isolation. Stress and exhaustion, as well as destructive negative emotions and lifestyles which accelerate deterioration of the body, have a ripple effect. They all affect the ecology of consciousness. A woman who decides to invest time and energy into restructuring her life to create room for play, pleasure, joy, beauty, and vitality gives a gift to her family, her friends, and everybody whose life she touches.

Creating Your Sanctuary

If you are over 50 you, as an ecosystem, might have survived some ecological disasters. My own body had to endure a few years of smoking in my youth, decades of recreational drinking, repeated burnout and overwhelm, grief, disappointment, and a number of very painful heartbreaks. You might have beliefs and attitudes which are pushing you into exhaustion and martyrdom. It is not easy to come into ecological awareness. It can be very humbling and sad, but it is what it is. The best thing about awareness is that once you know where you want to go, you can start investing energy and effort into restoring the vibrancy of your physical and spiritual environment.

When I first visited the Big Island of Hawaii, I was very disappointed to discover that the underwater world there was rather drab and bleak, with few fish and dark rocks instead of colorful corals. Then I went snorkeling in the marine preserve. Oh, what a difference it was! I was so delighted to see vibrant corals and swarms of playful and brightly colored fish.

It is probably impossible to ban fishing in the entire ocean. But the creation of marine preserves was a brilliant idea that helped save some areas of the underwater world in all its diverse and vital beauty. The same is with your inner space. It might be impossible to declare your whole body/mind space a sanctuary. But you might start with building a sanctuary in your heart, and then let your heart guide your journey to more vitality.

Let's Do This!

1. Imagine a beautiful nature sanctuary. In this sanctuary, only good energy is allowed to enter. There are rules of conduct. There is no defacing or destroying of nature resources. People are not allowed to bring their toxicity and emotional garbage there.

2. Fill this space with everything that promotes and encourages healing. It could be flowers and waterfalls. It could be healing crystals and beautiful music. Let yourself be really creative as you build your sanctuary.

3. Think of unconditional love. You can imagine a cloud of energy of unconditional love. You can think of a person who loves you unconditionally. (It could be a dog.) You can think about people you love unconditionally. Inhale love, and smile this love into your sanctuary, infusing every bit with love.

4. Place your hands over your heart. Smile into your heart. And with every breath, transfer the sanctuary you've just created into your heart until you know it is there.

5. Wrap love all around your heart. The Tao teaches wrapping the heart in green light to protect it. So wrap your heart in green healing light.

6. Imagine sitting quietly in your heart sanctuary, and feeling its beautiful, soothing, and serene energy. Now no matter what is going on in your life, you can always take a retreat in your heart and feel safe, protected, and guided.

7. Once you learn to get to your heart sanctuary easily, you can start growing it to expand to your entire body. Do not rush it. Let it expand and grow as you grow your confidence, and advance in your practices.

8. When you succeed in making your entire body feel like a nature sanctuary, you can practice creating a safe boundary around your body. Start with tapping into the energy of unconditional love by recalling memories of love. Think of the Universe, and imagine it contains a source of unconditional love flowing with abundance. Smile into this source and feel abundance. Guide this flow with your mind, heart, and eyes, and smile into your heart. As you smile into your heart, let this energy expand through your body, flow under and over your skin, and finally expand beyond your body.

9. Wrap yourself in a shimmering, glowing cocoon of unconditional love. Now, if you wish, you can expand this energy to the people you love — and maybe even let it envelop the entire planet.

Breathe in love, then let it flow.
Through the sky above and earth below.
Make your love so clean and clear
Feel it flowing like a river.
Nourishing what needs to grow
Washing away what needs to go.
In the sanctuary of love,
As below, as above.
Love is light. Life is flow.
As above, as below.

My dearest reader, thank you for joining me on this journey to sacred feminine vitality. If you've started thinking of yourself as nature and a part of the magnificent whole which is our planet Earth with everything that lives on it, I've accomplished my goal. As we part here, may your life force flow abundantly, and may you continue growing spiritually, mentally, and energetically. May you continue sharing your light and vibrancy, and blossom boldly in your unique ageless beauty through every delightful stage of your perfect life.

ABOUT THE AUTHOR

Anna Margolina, PhD

Scientist, Hypnotherapist, and Spiritual Teacher Dr. Anna earned her degree in medical biophysics from the Russian Medical University, and her PhD in biology in 1996. She worked as an esteemed editor and researcher for the Cosmetics and Medicine Journal in Russia, and a scientific advisor for cosmetics companies in the United States and Israel. Today, as the founder of Ageless with Anna, she continues her quest for feminine beauty and vitality — only now she focuses on ageless and timeless beauty, which is more than skin deep. She helps women regain their vitality and sensuality through ancient and modern tools such as Taoist Healing Love, hypnotherapy, and energy healing. She is a passionate champion for women of all ages who are eager to celebrate their natural feminine magic!

Anna Margolina, PhD, offers classes in sacred feminine vitality and healing love. Call her at 425-533-6456 to learn more. Or email her at anna@agelesswithanna.com.

Bibliography

Lewis, Thomas et al. *A General Theory of Love.* New York: Vintage Books, 2000.

Ekman, Paul. *Emotions Revealed: Recognizing Faces and Feelings to Improve Communication and Emotional Life.* Henry Holt and Company, 2003.

Hawkins, David R. *Power Vs. Force: The Hidden Determinants of Human Behavior.* Carlsbad, Calif: Hay House, 2002.

Noe, Alva. *Out of Our Heads: Why You Are Not Your Brain and Other Lessons from the Biology of Consciousness.* New York: Hill and Wang, 2009.

Chia, Mantak. *Healing Light of the Tao: Foundational Practices to Awaken Chi Energy.* Rochester, Vermont: Destiny Books, 2008.

Chia, Mantak and North, Deva. *Taoist Shaman: Practices from the Wheel of Life.* Rochester, Vermont: Destiny Books, 2010.

Chia, Mantak. *Taoist Cosmic Healing: Chi Kung Color Healing Principles for Detoxification and Rejuvenation.* Rochester, Vermont: Destiny Books, 2003.

Chia, Mantak. *Healing Love through the Tao: Cultivating Female Sexual Energy.* Chiang Mai, Thailand: Universal Healing Tao Publications, 1986.

Chia, Mantak. *Awaken Healing Energy through the Tao.* New York: Aurora Press, 1983.

Chia Mantak. *The Taoist Way to Rejuvenation.* New York: Healing Tao Books, 1986.

Chia, Mantak. *Iron Shirt Chi Kung I.* New York: Healing Tao Books, 1986.

The Complete I Ching. Translated by Huang, Alfred. Rochester, Vermont: Inner Traditions, 1998.

Selye, Hans. *The Stress of Life.* New York: McGraw-Hill Book Company, 1950.